'...EWS FOR YOU'

THE W...

D0359045

...ARSE board game

TV jesters Angus Deayton, Ian ...us quiz show 'Have I Got News ...this fabulous true to life board

...guests on opposing teams. Toss ...erton, and who joins Ian Hislop. ...then take turns at throwing a ...tions.

UNUSUAL HEADLINE

Seven patients die as flu vaccine shortage hampers hospitals

Explain the recent news story behind this headline. Then throw chuckle dice. **Odd** number means Ian Hislop has interrupted you and amuses himself by smugly explaining the news item while twiddling with his pencil. **Even** numbers means you have beaten him to it.

In summing up the scores Angus Deayton amusingly refers to your team as "This week's spring chickens". **Move forward 1.**

In summing up the scores Angus Deayton amusingly refers to your team as "This week's stuffed turkeys". **Go back to square 1.**

"ALLEGEDLY" SQUARE
You make an apparently libelous remark followed by the word "allegedly", safe in the knowledge that BBC lawyers will edit it out if it is in fact libelous. **Move forward 1.**

You refer to Jason Donovan's heterosexuality. Audience falls about. **Move forward 5.**

You have made a clever, quick witted ad lib. **Spin the Wheel of Smugness.**

Paul Merton persistently interrupts you in order to resurrect a surreal joke which died ten minutes ago. **Miss a turn** while Angus Deayton tries to find his place in the script.

You have made a clever, quick witted ad lib. **Spin the Wheel of Smugness.**

...ON'S ...DICE

...a joke ...which ...you ...ght and ...king a ...e. Throw ...ermine ...nidity. ...ward ...he score.

...P'S ...UGNESS.

...a cocktail stick ...the wheel to ...gness and self ...ward according

You say the 'F' word, safe in the knowledge that it will be bleeped out later. The audience goes wild. **Move forward 3.**

You make an apparently slanderous remark about the Royals, who never sue anyway. **Move forward 2.** (The words pot, kettle, and black immediately spring to mind)

Paul Merton persistently interrupts you in order to resurrect a surreal joke which died ten minutes ago. **Miss a turn** while Angus Deayton tries to find his place in the script.

Ian Hislop has made a joke at your expense. Quick as a flash you call him a "baldy git" **Spin the Wheel of Smugness.**

PHOTO CAPTION

Think of as many amusing captions for this photograph as you can in 20 seconds. Then just sit there looking pleased with yourself.

...E DICE

...funny throw a ...ow many laughs ...audience. If you ...tempt at topical ...and you move ...score an even ...Move forward

You fluff a joke and Paul Merton makes a fool of you. You go purple. **Move back 6.**

Angus Deayton refers to Paul Merton's commercial for Imperial Leather. Touché. **Move back 3.**

You refer to Angus Deayton's many appearances in commercials. Big laugh. **Move forward 3.**

You make an obligatory joke about Angus Deayton's clothes. Audience titters. **Move forward 1.**

THE ROYAL...
Di may
MIRROR'S MR SLEAZE

ROGER MELLIE

THE MAN ON THE TELLY

9.30 AM

HEY TOM!

ROGER. WHAT ARE YOU DOING IN SO EARLY?

I JUST HAD AN ABSOLUTELY **BRILLIANT** IDEA WHILE I WAS WATCHING BREAKFAST T.V.

THEY'VE GOT IT ALL WRONG TOM. BREAKFAST TELLY'S A LOAD OF CRAP. NO-ONE WANTS CHATTER AND EXERCISE AND RECIPES FIRST THING IN THE MORNING.

NO?

NO. IT'S TOO BRIGHT AND NOISY! EVERYONE'S TIRED AND HUNG OVER WHEN THEY WAKE UP.

PEOPLE WANT **THREE** THINGS WHEN THEY GET UP IN THE MORNING:- A CUP OF COFFEE, A BIT OF PEACE AND QUIET, AND A WANK.

A **WHAT**?!?

COME ON TOM. YOU KNOW WHAT IT'S LIKE WHEN YOU WAKE UP WITH A BIT OF A **STIFFY** AND YOU CAN'T GET YOUR PANTS ON.

BUT ROGER...

ANYWAY, THIS IS WHAT WE DO...

YOU KNOW HOW THEY HAVE THAT LITTLE CLOCK IN THE CORNER OF THE SCREEN ALL THE TIME, TICKING AWAY ALL MORNING.

WELL WE GET RID OF THAT.

INSTEAD, WE HAVE A LITTLE PICTURE OF A SAUCY BIRD, DANCING AND GETTING HER KIT OFF!

BRILLIANT ISN'T IT! NO MATTER WHAT TIME YOU GET UP, YOU CAN SWITCH ON THE BOX AND HAVE A QUICK HAND SHANDY!

BUT ROGER... THAT'S **PORNOGRAPHY!**

OH NO - WE'LL DO ALL THE NEWS AND STUFF AS WELL...

BUT WE'LL ALL TALK **REALLY, REALLY** QUIETLY IN CASE ANY OF THE VIEWERS HAVE GOT A HEADACHE

ROGER. YOU'RE WASTING YOUR TIME ON STUPID IDEAS LIKE THAT. YOU SHOULD BE CONCENTRATING ON YOUR NEW SHOW

REMEMBER - WE'RE FILMING A PILOT FOR CHANNEL 4 TODAY!

OH **SHIT**! THAT REMINDS ME. I'VE GOT A HAIR-DRESSER'S APPOINTMENT AT TEN!

HAIRDRESSER?! IS THAT REALLY NECESSARY ROGER?

DON'T WORRY TOM. I KNOW WHAT I'M DOING. MY NEW SHOW IS GOING TO BE A **BIG** SUCCESS. CHANNEL 4 WILL LOVE IT

WELL, WHATEVER YOU DO, DON'T BE LATE. WE START THE RECORDING AT ONE O'CLOCK SHARP.

"PLOT" EXPLANATION INTERLUDE...

ROGER CERTAINLY IS TAKING THIS NEW SHOW OF HIS SERIOUSLY. I WONDER WHAT IT'S ALL ABOUT

ANYWAY, IT BETTER BE GOOD. THE COMMISSIONING EDITOR OF CHANNEL 4 IS COMING TODAY TO WATCH THE RECORDING.

THINKS... HMMM! PERHAPS, AS THE DIRECTOR, I SHOULD HAVE ASKED ROGER WHAT THIS NEW SHOW WAS CALLED. BUT NEVER MIND. I'M SURE HE KNOWS WHAT HE'S DOING

ANYWAY...

KNOCK KNOCK!

AH! THAT'LL BE THE COMMISSIONING EDITOR OF CHANNEL 4 NOW

DELIVERY OF BIRDS FOR MR MELLIE

BIRDS? WHAT DO YOU MEAN?

"ONE HUNDRED BIRDS", IT SAYS HERE, "WITH BIG TITS. DELIVER TO F.T.V." I'VE GOT THEM OUTSIDE IN THE LORRY. JUST SIGN HERE WILL YOU

ONE HUNDRED BIRDS WITH BIG TITS... WHAT THE HELL IS ROGER UP TO?

AAH! THERE YOU ARE TOM. WHAT ON EARTH IS GOING ON OUTSIDE? THERE'S NUDE WOMEN WITH LARGE BREASTS EVERYWHERE. NOTHING TO DO WITH THIS NEW SHOW I HOPE. WE DON'T APPROVE OF ANY SEXIST RUBBISH ON CHANNEL 4 YOU KNOW

OH... ERM...

ANYWAY. WHAT'S IT ALL ABOUT THEN TOM, THIS NEW SHOW OF ROGER'S?

WELL... ERM... PERHAPS ROGER OUGHT TO EXPLAIN IT HIMSELF...

TO BE QUITE HONEST I'M STILL 'IN THE DARK' A LITTLE MYSELF. BUT ROGER SHOULD BE HERE ANY MINUTE.

HI TOM. ARE WE READY TO ROLL?

ROGER. WHAT THE **HELL** ARE YOU DRESSED LIKE **THAT** FOR? AND WHY ARE THERE NAKED WOMEN WITH LARGE BREASTS EVERYWHERE?

THIS IS ALL FOR MY NEW SHOW TOM. **THE BRISTOL MAZE**

IT'S A BIT LIKE THE CRYSTAL MAZE, BUT IT'S GOT LOADS OF TITS IN IT!

WE BLINDFOLD THE CONTESTANTS AND THEY HAVE TO **FEEL** THEIR WAY OUT OF A ROOM FULL OF NAKED BIRDS WITH GREAT BIG KNOCKERS WITHOUT GETTING A HARD ON!

WELL I'M SORRY MR MELLIE, BUT THERE IS ABSOLUTELY NO WAY CHANNEL 4 COULD DEVOTE PRIME TIME TO SUCH A PATHETIC IDEA.

BUT WE MIGHT BE ABLE TO SLOT IT INTO OUR NEW 'BIG NOISY BREAKFAST SHOW'.

ZZZZZZZ ZZZZZZ

YOU SEE, THE PROBLEM WITH BREAKFAST T.V. IS THAT IT'S NOT **SEXY** ENOUGH. YOU KNOW WHAT IT'S LIKE WHEN YOU WAKE UP IN THE MORNING WITH A BIG STIFF ON...

4

THE BIG
BELL END

*A platter of cheesey bits
from issues 58 to 63*

Edited by Chris Donald

Written and illustrated by
Chris Donald, Graham Dury, Simon Thorp and Simon Donald

With contributions from
Davey Jones and John Fardell

Photography by Colin Davison

ISBN 1 870870 64 6

Published in Great Britain by John Brown Publishing Limited,
The Boathouse, Crabtree Lane, Fulham, London, SW6 6LU.

First printed September 1995.

6

Lay off the drink drivers

Why do police and magistrates always come down so hard on motorists who have accidents after they have been drinking. Clearly having had a few drinks a person's ability to drive is greatly reduced. So surely it is understandable when these people have the odd mishap. It is the *sober* motorists, who despite not drinking *still* manage to crash their cars, who the authorities ought to be clamping down on.

D. McLure
Arbroath

Isn't it about time we sorted out the sides for the next world war? I think Japan should be on our side this time, and Germany can have America, 'cos they tend to kill quite a few of our soldiers no matter which side they're on.

P. Lancer
Rochester

I made a spectacle of myself

My boss sent me to collect some glasses the other day. After visiting every opticians in town my mistake suddenly dawned on me. I'm a barmaid, and the glasses he was referring to were empty beer glasses.
How he laughed when he realised what I'd done, before sacking me on the spot.

G. Canty (Miss)
Hebden Bridge

My wife went to Amsterdam the other day, and I asked her to bring me back some 'hard core'. Imagine my disappointment when she staggered home clutching a sack of broken stones suitable for forming building foundations. Do I win £5.

J. C. Brighouse
Nuneaton

LetterBocks
Viz Commick
P.O. Box 1 PT
Newcasle upon Tyne
NE99 1PT

Please may I take the opportunity of your letters page to thank Cilla Black for recommending that I switch from gas to electric heating. I took her advice, and my house is now unbearably stuffy. cold in the winter, too hot on mild days, there are large stains on the wall above my heaters and my heating bill has trebled.
I wonder whether Cilla has suffered similar problems herself with electric central heating at her large mansion house in Buckinghamshire.

L. Erikson
Hartlepool

There don't seem to have been any pictures on the letters page so far. It would be nice to break it up a little with something. How about a picture of a rabbit?

J. Dodds
Ford

* I'm sorry Mr Dodds, but we can't find any pictures of rabbits. But here's a rather nice view of some sheep, in a field.

I'm sick of unemployed people moaning. I for one took Norman Tebbit's advice, got on my bike, and now I'm the Olympic 5000m Individual Pursuit Cycling Champion.

Chris Boardman
Liverpool

Prince Charles has proved to us all that he is not a man fit to be King. Who in their right mind would climb over Princess Di to get to Camilla Parker Bowles? If I had a bird like Di you wouldn't catch me playing away from home.
I reckon he might be a queer. What do other readers think?

Mr L.O.T. Ocean-Wave
Birmingham

Brighten up these boring hospitals

Wouldn't hospitals be much brighter, more cheerful places if doctors and nurses dressed in brightly coloured clowns outfits or harlequin suits, instead of sombre white coats and green costumes. I for one would feel much happier being given the news of a tragic bereavement by someone wearing a red nose and face paint.

B. Murphy
Morpeth

Give way to baldies

As the onset of incontinence and loss of hair are usually simultaneous in middle aged men, I always let bald people go in front of me when there's a queue for the toilet.

A. Adderstone, 18
Bemerside

If I was Ian Botham I wouldn't walk from one end of the country to another to raise money for charity. I'd get my fucking hair cut and stop looking like a girl.

C. O'Connell
Nottingham

When in France the English should continue to drive on the left hand side of the road, providing they switch their hazard warning lights on and observe a maximum speed limit of 15 miles per hour. (This could be converted into kilometres per hour if the French wish to be pedantic) I believe this would greatly reduce the number of likely accidents once the new channel tunnel is opened.

P. Duel
Manningtree, Essex

The new 'Cindy Crawford Workout Video' is bloody marvellous. I've only had it a fortnight and I've already got a right arm like Arnold Schwarzenegger.

B. Beater
St Anne's

Many thanks to the British Rail employees whose dishevelled appearance, unhelpful attitudes and objectionable behavior generally brightened up what would have been an otherwise tedious train journey from London to York recently. Special thanks are due to the Scottish buffet attendant who swore at me when I tried to pay for a cup of tea with a five pound note.

H. Chaparal
Grosmont

Wedding day memories

Why doesn't the Prince of Wales stick with tradition and have his wife beheaded. This would solve at a stroke the problem of whether or not she should become Queen.

Neil Wood
Blackburn

Whatever happened to the old fashioned tradition of a 'lucky chimney sweep' appearing at weddings to wish the happy couple happiness and good fortune in their married life together?

'Bert the Sweep'
Lucky Chimney Sweep
(Weddings a speciality)
155 Tudor Road
Leicester LE3 5JH

It must be difficult to produce such a substantial magazine for the exceptionally low cover price of one pound. Is there any prospect of a price rise in the near future? I for one would welcome such a move.

B. Smith
Fulchester

* There are no plans for a price increase, Mr Smith. However if the Chancellor of the Exchequer were to levy VAT on magazines, as has been suggested recently, an increase would be unavoidable, and we would naturally take that opportunity to bung our profits up as well.

«Top Tips»

RECORD the sound of your wife having a orgasm, then listen to the tape through headphones the next time you make love. That way you can have sex without waking her up.

Frank Wilson
Southend

PRETEND you don't live in Tottenham by walking around Tottenham with an A to Z asking people for directions.

Simone Glover
Tottenham

MOTORISTS. Pressing your 'fog lights' switch a second time after the fog has cleared will actually turn the fog lights off.

J. C.
Luton

'FAST FOOD' restaurants. Don't waste valuable milk powder making 'milk shakes'. Chicken fat is much cheaper, and just as delicious once the sugar is added.

A. Warnington
Hampton

AVOID cutting yourself while clumbsily slicing vegetables by getting someone else to hold them while you chop away.

I. J. Alexander
Birmingham

FOOL corner shop owners into thinking that you live nearby long after you have moved out of the area, by making frequent early morning and evening visits to his shop for cigarettes, milk, bread and other groceries.

M. Renshaw
London

BEAT bicycle theft by towing a horse box behind your bike. When you stop, simply padlock the cycle securely inside the horse box.

Don Brayford
Withersfield, Suffolk

WHEN packing fragile objects in a box popcorn makes an ideal replacement for expensive polystyrene 'chips'.

Mr Edwards
Leighton Buzzard

SUNDAY Sport editors. Write your own fucking letters page.

A. Grieved
Fulchester

New tragedy rocks Queen

A new tragedy has hit rock group Queen.

Hot on the heels of the tragic death of singer Freddie Mercury, guitarist Brian May has spoken out for the first time about another disaster that has befallen the group.

CHILD

For rocker Brian has revealed that as a child he suffered from nits.

KENNY

Now 42 and living with long time girlfriend Anitta Dobson, the hair condition struck Brian when he was eleven. "It was a nightmare. I had to go and see the school nurse. She gave me some powder for it, and within a couple of days it had cleared up", May has told close friends. But although the hair lice have gone, May must forever live his life in the shadow of nits.

GLITTER BAND

"It's difficult for Brian, because he knows that he could, one day, get nits again", a source close to the group confided yesterday.

DI IN 'ZOO MONKEY BLOW JOB' SHOCKER

The vicious publicity battle which has been raging between the Prince of Wales and his embittered wife Princess Di took a sordid turn today when an Australian magazine published explicit photographs which it alleges show the Princess having oral sex with a monkey in a zoo.

The blurry pictures, taken from a considerable distance with a telephoto lens, were sent to the New South Wales offices of Australian magazine 'Viz'. They are believed to have been sent by a close colleague of Prince Charles, and are the latest attempt by the Prince of Wales to undermine his wife's popularity.

BITTER

In a bitter public feud lasting several months the Royal rivals have traded stories with the press, each designed to damage the other's reputation. Di, it is alleged, with the help of her close allies, has leaked sensitive information to the tabloid press aimed at discrediting her husband and skuttling his chances of becoming King. Meanwhile Charles is believed to have orchestrated a similar campaign aimed at branding Diana a tramp and an unfit mother.

MILD

We were sent copies of the Monkeygate pictures as long ago as June 1991, but we declined the offer to publish them, refusing to be pawns in the bitter Royal slagging match between Charles and Di. Instead, we

CAMILLA: Climbed tree for kinky love session with Charles

More FILTH on the Royals

sent them to our wholly owned Australian subsiduary and suggested they publish them instead.

HEAVY

Buckingham Palace yesterday claimed to have no knowledge of the pictures. "If Diana has sucked off a monkey, which wouldn't entirely surprise me, I wouldn't particularly want to see the pictures anyway", a spokesman for the Queen told us.

STOUT

But the signs are that Princess Di's camp are preparing to hit back with a major revelation about Prince Charles and his alleged mistress Camilla Parker Bowles. A private detective claiming to have been hired by Princess Di, last night offered us exclusive pictures which he claims were taken of Camilla and Charles at a polo meeting in 1990 – almost a year before the Monkeygate pictures broke. The detective, who refused to be named, claimed that his pictures showed Charles, Camilla and a polo pony in a compromising position.

TUBBY

"There's one great shot of Charles taking the pony from behind, while Camilla is up a tree pissing on them", he boasted.

OBESE

As a family paper loyal to our Royal family we refuse to print such scandalous and filthy photographs. We handed the pictures, together with our dossier on the case, to the editor of the Australian 'Viz' magazine.

10

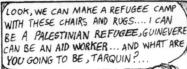

The MODERN PARENTS

TARQUIN AND GUINEVERE ARE HAVING THEIR PLAY-SESSION....

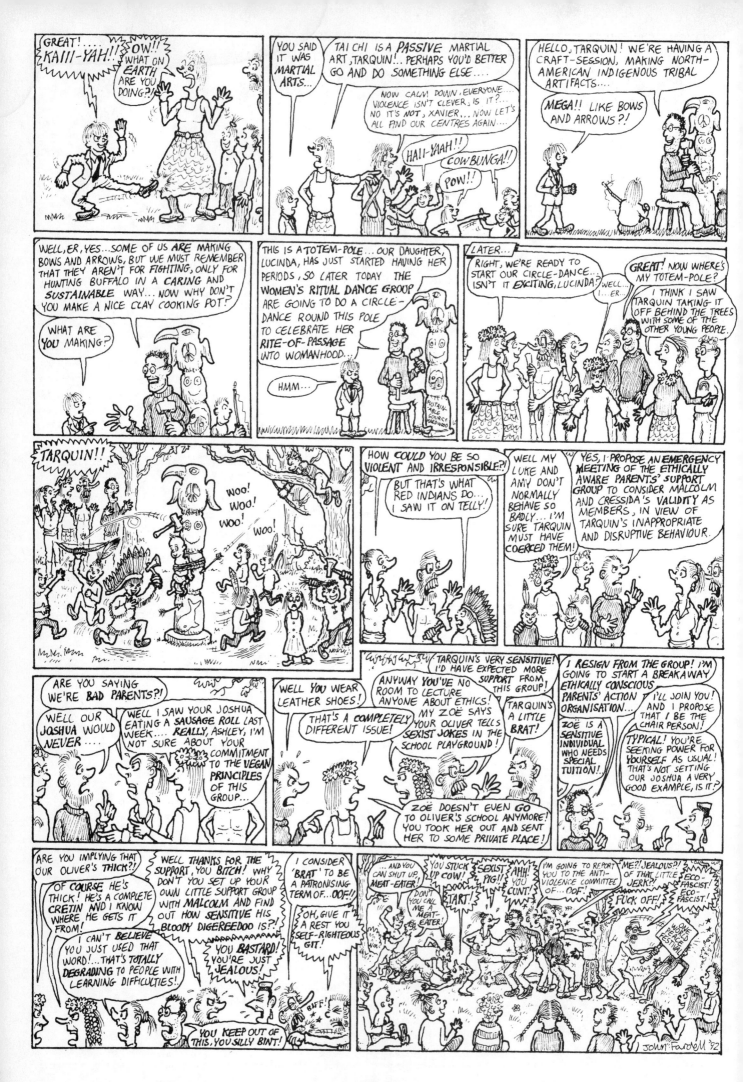

FRANKENSTAR MUST DIE!

A showbusiness hurricane is brewing over Variety Club plans to create a 'Frankenstein' style celebrity monster using the remains of dead stars from the past.

Plans for the showbusiness monster were hatched by fund raisers hoping to raise extra cash towards the Variety Club's Sunshine Coach appeal. But there is growing unrest among showbusiness personalities concerned that a man-made celebrity monster, assembled using limbs and organs from dead stars, would be in bad taste. And alarm bells are ringing after some insiders admitted that the monster may go wrong, and kill the very children that it was setting out to help.

RISK

"There is always a risk that an experiment like this could go wrong. The monster may not know its own strength, or scientists may accidentally give it the wrong brain or something", admitted concerned star Ernie Wise last night.

VARIETY

The variety club is believed to have already begun work on the 'monster' at a castle in North Wales belonging to comedian Jimmy Tarbuck.

Tarby – castle

Storm over celebrity monster set to do charity work for kids

And according to some reports, Tarbuck's shopping list for the proposed 'Frankenstar' includes:

- **HAIR** from the late great comedian Frankie Howerd.
- The **CHEEKY GRIN** of the late Bennie Hill.
- **LEGS** removed from musical hall great Arthur Askey.
- **FEET** from giant comic Tommy Cooper.
- And Eric Morcambe's glasses.

Once the monster is complete pioneering Variety Club scientists plan to bring it to life by harnessing the power of an electrical storm. They then plan to tour the country, doing sell-out charity shows to raise funds for needy kids.

VAMPIRE

This is not the first time that a fund raising organisation run by the stars has attempted such an ambitious project. In 1989, amidst a storm of publicity, the Lords Taverners

announced plans to make a vampire out of Peter Sellers. The project cost several million pounds to finance, but ran aground when Sellers failed to wake up when it got dark.

An artists impression of how the monster will look when it emerges from Castle Tarbuck.

The hands of the late great DAVID NIXON will give it breathtaking conjuring ability.

The singing, dancing legs of music hall legend ARTHUR ASKEY will give it 'all round' entertainment value, with terrific family appeal.

The feet and shoes of the immortal TOMMY COOPER will come to life once more as the undead creature takes the stage in numerous charity shows.

We will laugh again at the saucy antics of BENNY HILL as the beast breathes new life into his cheeky grin.

CAREFUL. IT MIGHT BE A TRAP.

SNATCH OF THE DAY

BBC Match of the Day presenters' plans for a well earned summer break have been dealt a cruel blow by heartless thieves.

Soccer pundits Jimmy Hill, Trevor Brooking, John Motson and Alan Hansen had planned to get away from it all during a quiet boating break on the Norfolk Broads.

TRILLION

But disaster struck when thieves broke into their boat and stole equipment including a fire extinguisher, life

jackets and a radio, the total haul valued at over £400. The TV football pals are said to be heartbroken and may even have to consider cancelling the trip.

ZILLION

A police spokesman said youngsters were probably responsible for the raid in which a padlock was forced and one window broken.

Barry Davies - he used to be a dentist. And that's true.

"The equipment taken would have little or no value to anyone else", he told us.

I'VE BEDDED TH

A 52 year old out patient at a West Midlands psychiatric hospital has spilled the beans on her steamy affairs with the saucy stars of the TV puppet shows.

For the last 25 years Dulcie Bagshaw claims to have lived a sordid life as a TV puppet groupie, jumping in and out of bed with some of the biggest names in children's television.

HORNY

Here, for the first time, she blows the lid clean off the horny, porny puppets who millions of innocent kids watch on TV every day.

RANDY

"Kids love TV shows like Rainbow, The Wombles and Bill & Ben. But if their parents could see what I have seen, they'd switch off in disgust.

PAUL

My first experience with a TV puppet came when I was only 14. I had been to the theatre to watch a stage version of The Sooty Show. Afterwards a group of us went backstage to get autographs. Somehow I ended up alone in Sooty's dressing room.

NANETTE

Sooty offered me a drink. I don't know what it was, but I was soon feeling dizzy. The next thing I knew Sooty was standing naked in front of me, holding his magic wand. I'll never forget the words he spoke. "Izzy wizzy, let's get busy".

SOOTY

That evening I had gone to see the Sooty show as a child. But when I awoke the next morning in Sooty's hotel room, I was a woman. I had bitten the forbidden fruit of sex with TV puppets, and now I wanted more. Over the next ten years I must have slept with over a hundred TV puppets. I wasn't fussy. Life became one long party, an endless whirl of late nights, drink and TV puppets.

You name them, I slept with them. Bill and Ben, The Woodentops, The Clangers, Orville the Duck, Joe 90. The list is endless. TV puppets came and went. The affairs were purely physical, strictly no strings attached. Until the day I met Basil Brush.

BASIL

Basil was a joy to be with. He used to love to fondle my "bum bum" as he called it, and he couldn't keep his foxy fingers of my brush. But he soon became obsessed with me, and even began following me around.

SYBIL

In the end we had a dreadful scene in a restaurant. I remember he was sitting on the bar. He was screaming and shouting, and he'd even threatened to kill himself if I didn't come back to him. Eventually Rodney Bewes arrived and took him home. I never saw Basil again after that.

SAD

I was sad to see the end of Rainbow. That show meant a lot to me. More than you could imagine. For I had got to know Bungle, Zippy and George intimately during a long and torrid affair which had lasted many years. I loved all three of them – on one occasion *all at once*.

Dulcie with her first love Sooty (left) and Sweep, and surrounded by the stars of Rainbow (left to right) George, Zippy and Bungle. Inset - Basil Br

SUMMERS

It was a hot and sticky summer's evening, but I had no idea just how hot and sticky I was going to get as I made my way to the Rainbow dressing room at the BBC Television Centre in West London. I'd been invited back for drinks with the Rainbow puppets after a chance meeting with Zippy in a cocktail bar. When I arrived I could tell straight away that all three TV puppets had already had quite a lot to drink.

DIAMOND

I was feeling hot and horny so I stripped off down to my bra and knickers and stretched out on the settee. Next thing I knew Zippy had undone his zip and was licking his lips. Bungle and George needed no more encouragement and soon both were as naked as I was.

HATHAWAY

Before long Zippy and George were fondling my heaving breasts while Bungle the bear took me roughly from behind. I climaxed again and again until I almost passed out. Then Zippy took over while George, the pink hippopotamus, paid special attention to my love buttons. Just when I thought I could

come no more, Zippy exploded inside of me, taking me to heights of ecstasy that before I had only ever dreamed of.

ATTENTION

I had never really paid any attention to Ray Allan's puppet Lord Charles. He didn't strike me as being my type. Until one day we met in the lift at Thames TV. Ray was afraid of lifts, so he took the stairs up to the top floor.

AT EASE

As the doors of the lift slid closed I found myself alone with Lord Charles. What happened next took me by surprise. As the lift began to move, Lord Charles suddenly pressed the 'stop' button, and it shuddered to a halt, throwing me into his arms.

LIPS

A strange force seemed to draw our lips together, and as we kissed passionately I felt a small wooden hand slip into my blouse and expertly undo my bra, which slid down around my ankles.

AROUSED

I could feel that Lord Charles was already aroused. His bulging manhood was practically bursting out of his

14

TV PUPPETS!

Seedy sex lives of the children's telly favourites

Lord Charles - his manhood was enormous.

small, pinstriped trousers. I struggled frantically to release it, until suddenly it sprang forth, like a coiled python.

ENORMOUS

It was that enormous I almost passed out. It was the biggest wooden penis I had ever seen. I simply had to have it inside me. I was already sopping wet as, with one powerful stroke of his 'silly arse', he forced it into me. My earth shattering climax was over in seconds, ecstasy exploding through my veins.

LUST

That day Lord Charles and I abandoned ourselves to sexual lust, pure and simple. Neither of us said a word. Neither of us have spoken about it since, and neither of us ever will.

CONQUEST

There was one sexual conquest that I never achieved. I had already slept with four of the five Tracey brothers out of Thunderbirds. And their *equipment* had been just as impressive as anything that they used on their International Rescue missions, I can tell you! But there was one Tracey brother who had always eluded my grasp.

WISDOM

I began to wonder whether I was losing my touch, until one night I was staying on Tracey Island when I heard the sound of laughter and splashing coming from the swimming pool. I crept out, and there in the moonlight was my

unconquered Thunderbird pilot, wrapped in a tender embrace... with Brains!

TEBBIT

I'm not prepared to name that puppet, suffice to say that the only 'bird' he had eyes for was Thunder*bird* 4.

COOK

Mind you, I have nothing against gay TV puppets. In fact, one of my most fulfilling sexual experiences took place with a female puppet – Lady Penelope.

WAITER

She had offered me a lift into town in her big, pink car. As we were driving along Parker pressed a button and curtains automatically closed around the windows. We were alone. Suddenly Lady Penelope dabbed her stiff, plastic hand on my thigh.

MAITRE D'

At first I was repulsed. This was a *woman* TV puppet touching me. But slowly my fear began to subside, and waves of pleasure began to wash over me. Penelope's plastic fingers began to awaken in me feelings that I didn't know were there. It was my first time with a woman TV puppet, but Lady Penelope was able to

pleasure me in a way that only a woman could.

THOMAS

I had always fancied Thomas the Tank Engine, but I had never dreamt that I might one day get the opportunity to sleep with him. That was until I met the Fat Controller at a TV puppet party to celebrate Lamb Chop's birthday. The Fat Controller invited me to come and visit Thomas and his friends on the Island of Sodor. I didn't need asking twice!

SHY

When I first met Thomas he was shy, not at all like I'd expected him to be. One day he'd been shunting trucks at the big station when he asked me if I wanted to come for a ride along his branch line. I was up in his cab like a shot!

OIL

After a few miles he stopped in a siding and we began to chat. Eventually the subject got on to sex, and to my surprise Thomas admitted to me that he had never been with a woman before.

MILK

I took this as my signal to pull off, and slowly began to

slide down his zip and gently slip off his jeans. He was already aroused. I have never seen such a magnificent train's cock. I almost passed out. It was easily eleven inches in length, and my fingers could barely touch around it's massive girth.

BUTTER

We made passionate love for what seemed like an eternity. Thomas puffed and panted and blew his whistle as he shunted his load in and out of my love tunnel. Then suddenly I became aware of somebody watching us.

CHEESE

Sure enough, I looked up to see Gordon, Edward and James the red engine had stopped nearby and were watching us. That turned me on even more. I beckoned them over and invited them to join in. They didn't need asking twice, I can tell you.

YOGHURT

I must have passed out, but the next thing I remember was waking up to see Thomas, Gordon, Henry and James all pulling the biggest train you have ever seen.

CREAM

I lost count of the number of orgasms I had as the TV puppet railway engines continued to take me in turn for what seemed like an eternity. Then the helicopter joined in.

DEREK AND THE DOMINOES

I must have passed out again, because when I awoke I was in a mental hospital, with electrodes on my head.

Next week: How I fell pregnant to Noggin the Nog, and the Clangers give me my first weightless orgasm in space. And Great Uncle Bulgaria gives me one up the shitter.

LADY PENELOPE
'pleasured me'

SCOTT TRACEY
'Impressive equipment'

PARKER
He pressed button

"The other day I played chess with Mr Kipling. 'What an exceedingly good chess set', I mused".

For over a hundred years families have enjoyed Mr Kipling's cakes. Now, the excellence of those cakes has been captured for ever in a superb commemorative chess set, crafted in the finest marble and alabaster, a fitting tribute to the man and his cakes.

To Cherish and enjoy

Every piece in this set has been expertly sculpted and detailed making it a pleasure to pick up, and a joy to behold. This is truly a chess set to cherish and enjoy. A chess set that Mr Kipling himself would be proud to own.

The board is in itself a work of art. Hand carved from carefully selected pieces of former Brazilian rain forest, this immaculate hardwood base doubles as a carrying case and provides a fitting home for these unique cake chess pieces.

Accompanying the set is a fascinating booklet that charts the history of Mr Kipling cakes, and introduces each piece in turn. From the Bramley Apple Pie pawns, obediently standing in line, ready to make the greatest sacrifice a Kipling cake can make. To the gallant knights, hewn in the form of the classic Jam Tart. Ever popular, ever true. A battle proud warrior, fit to lead his army of courageous cakes. Each piece an individual cake, with its own qualities, its own strengths. Together they form an invincible army of cake.

Affordably low price

The Mister Kipling Cake Chess Set is available exclusively by subscription from the Trebor Mint. Subscribers will receive one piece each month at an affordably low price of only £96.50. What's more, the board and information booklet are yours free, for a one off payment of only £29.99.

THE
🌿 MR 🌿
KIPLING
CHESS SET

Magnificently detailed, fine marble and alabaster sculptures. Capturing for all eternity the beauty and elegance of Mr Kipling's cakes.

This will be a limited edition set, an heirloom quality work of art that is guaranteed to appreciate in value with the passage of years, and we therefore urge you to subscribe NOW to avoid disappointment.

This is a rare opportunity to own a chess set that will not only excite devotees of the game, but also one that will delight anyone interested in Mr Kipling's cakes.

The King – represented by the Bakewell Slice, truly the ruler of the cake Kingdom. A masterpiece among Mr Kipling cakes. Standing proud behind a shield of icing, he sits atop his double thrown, crafted in the powerful image of the foil cake cup. Majestically the King surveys his army.

Shown smaller than actual size.

The Bishop. With deserved respect our artist has chosen to represent this piece with the Fondant Fancy. Sitting either side of his King and Queen, the Bishop, resplendent in his fluted paper case, brings dignity and humanity to the game.

The Rook. Sturdy and solid, he signifies strength, as represented by Mr Kipling's Jaffa Finger. One of the most popular of Mr Kipling's cakes, the detailing of this piece simply has to be seen to be believed.

16

20 THINGS YOU NEVER KNEW ABOUT ROOFS

They're on houses and huts, sheds and shopping centres. Angry people hit them, sales go through them. And arseholes jump off them with parachutes.

Yes, they're roofs. And whether you love them or hate them, there's simply no ignoring them. But what do you really know about these amazing structures that form or cover the top of a building? Here's twenty things you probably never new about roofs...

1 A 'flat roof' is not necessarily the roof of a flat. It is in fact a new, horizontal style roof which either leaks or has puddles on it, which recently replaced the old fashioned, cumbersome 'pitched roofs' which had previously been used, and had protected buildings from the weather without any problems for several hundred years.

2 A 'roofer' is a shifty, suspicious looking character who occasionally appears at your door with a broken slate in his hand and claims that, despite visual evidence to the contrary, it has fallen off your roof.

3 Next thing you know he'll charge you £25 to lean a ladder on your house, climb up it and make a banging noise for ten minutes, before pissing off to the pub.

4 If you call a 'Thatcher' to come and mend your roof, don't expect a bitter former lady Prime Minister, her drunken husband or her half-wit son to turn up with a ladder. A thatcher is in fact a traditional craftsman who will attempt to repair leaks with clumps of straw.

5 If someone tells you that they've just spent a night 'on the tiles', they haven't necessarily slept on the roof. Unless they are a prisoner in one of Britain's overcrowded jails, in which case they very probably have, and the remains of the roof are probably lying in the exercise yard.

6 If the vicar asks his choir to 'raise the roof', he isn't trying to get building work done on the cheap. He's simply asking them to sing loudly.

7 If the vicar asks you to contribute to his 'steeple restoration fund', he *is* trying to get building work done on the cheap, by getting *you* to pay for it.

8 'So long as you've got a roof over your head', someone once said. But orthodox Jews may well disagree. Their religion dictates that they cannot have a roof over their heads on a Saturday, or something like that.

9 And they don't eat pork. Not even sausages.

10 Houses are built from the bottom, upwards, finishing with the roof. This is to allow for any inaccuracy in the height of the building. For if the roof was built first, a couple of inches too high, then it would leave a small gap at the bottom of the walls. The only exception is Australia where they build the roof first, and have Christmas Day in the middle of June.

11 Roofs are no strangers to the UK pop charts. In 1970 The Supremes climbed 'Up The Ladder To The Roof', reaching No. 6 in the Top Ten.

12 And more recently Lionel Ritchie was 'Dancing On The Ceiling', which was sort of similar.

13 Indeed, in another remarkable pop/roof tie-in, The Beatles hit record 'Let It Be' was recorded on a roof.

14 However, 'Fiddler On The Roof' was not a

copy cat album by scruffy violinist Nigel Kennedy. It was in fact the hit musical in which that bloke with a beard called Toblerone or something sang that song that went "If I was a rich man, yaddle diddle diddle, yaddle yaddle diddle diddle dum. All day long I'd biddy biddy bum, if I was a wealthy man", etc.

15 People on 'That's Life' frequently claim that their dog can say "roof".

16 And "sausages".

17 Mountaineer Chris Bonnington has on more than one occasion climbed to the 'roof of the world' – the Himalayan mountains. And he occasionally comes back with the same number of people he set out with.

18 Singer David Bowie's roof maintenance bills are enormous. That's because Dave has 3 roofs. One on each of his houses in Australia, Mustique and Switzerland.

19 In fact he's got 4 roofs, if you count the roof of his mouth, with which he has sung such hits as 'Alvin Stardust' and 'Space Odessey'.

20 There is no cockney rhyming slang expression for roof. That's because 'roof', along with 'orange' and 'motorbike', are the only three words in the English language with which no other word rhymes. In fact, the Oxford English Dictionary have offered a £10,000 reward to anyone who can think of a word that rhymes with roof. If you think you know one, send it to The Oxford English Dictionary, Roof Rhyme £10,000 Reward Department, Oxford University Press, Horse Hoof Lane, Oxford. Please mark your envelope 'I've thought of a word that rhymes with roof'.

I'M SORRY. YOU'LL HAVE TO SPEAK UP. I'M ON MY MOBILE.

FRY'S TURKISH DELIGHT

STEPHEN! YOU'RE THE BRAINIEST BOY AT CAMBRIDGE UNIVERSITY AND YOU KNOW ALL THE BIGGEST WORDS...

MNYAAH!

...AND AS A CONSEQUENCE, THE DEAN OF THE FACULTY OF BIG WORDS HAS DECIDED TO PRESENT YOU, AS A GIFT, THIS LARGE PILE OF TURKISH DELIGHT

MNYAAH! WHAT SPLENDIDITY

MOIST, PINK AND FLUFFY

OH, BY THE WAY, FRY, SCULLION, THE PORTER SAYS YOUR CONFECTION IS CAUSING AN OBSTRUCTION IN THE QUAD

OH, TISH AND PISH AND... IF I MIGHT MAKE SO BOLD... TUMMY RUBBISH

I'M SORRY, FRY, BUT SCULLION IS ADAMANT...

...UNLESS YOU REMOVE IT WITHIN ONE HOUR YOU WILL BE THROWN OUT OF CAMBRIDGE UNIVERSITY...

...GOOD DAY TO YOU

HMMM! WHAT A VERITABLE CONUNDRUM. MY BRAIN IS WELL AND TRULY TEASED, TICKLED AND, INDEED, TESTED BY THIS BIJOU LITTLE PROBLEMETTE

I MUST WASTE NOT ONE JOT NOR INDEED ONE TITTLE OF TIME IN RESOLVING HOW TO MOVE THIS SWEETMEAT FROM HITHER... MNYAAH... TO YON

SUDDENLY...

MNYAAH!!

GOOD DAY, STOUT YEOMAN. I WONDER IF I MAY INTERRUPT YOUR HORTICULTUR-AL ENDEAVOURS TO ENSURE IF I MIGHT COMMANDEERE, MOMENTARILY, THIS FINE AND... MNYAAH...STURDY WHEELBARROW

EH!?!

FUCK OFF, YOU LANKY, BENT-NOSED PONCE

Z

FIDDLE-DE-DEE AND FIDDLE STICKS. WHAT LOUTISH BEHAVIOUR

SO...

WELL SPANK MY BOTTOM AND CALL ME ABIGAIL. I'M BLOWED IF I KNOW HOW TO MOVE THIS LITTLE MONT DE BONBONS

ONE HOUR LATER...

WELL, I SEE BY THE CLOCK THAT TIME, THE OLD ADVERSARY HAS BEATEN ME

OH, BOTHER! HERE'S THE CHANCELLOR! MY GOOSE, IF YOU'LL PARDON THE CLICHÉ, IS WELL AND TRUELY COOKED...

...UNLESS...

AH! FRY. I'M GLAD YOU'VE MANAGED TO MOVE ALL OF YOUR TURKISH DELIGHT!..

MNYAAH!

...I DIDN'T WANT TO HAVE TO THROW YOU OUT OF THE UNIVERSITY FOR SUCH A PALTRY REASON

WAIT A MOMENT. WHY ARE YOU WEARING A DRESS, FRY?

ERM... I'M REHEARSING AN HILARIOUS AND SPLENDIDLY CHUCKLESOME SKIT FOR THE FOOTLIGHTS WITH EMMA THOMPSON AND TONYPOO SLATTERY

AH, SPLENDID! THERE'S ALWAYS BEEN A GOOD TRADITION OF TRANSVESTISM IN THE FOOT-LIGHTS. CARRY ON, FRY

WELL... IT SEEMS THERE REMAINS ONLY ONE AVENUE LEFT OPEN TO ME... VIS A VIS THIS TURKISH DELIGHT...

SO...

BARP!

QUACK!

SUDDENLY...

I SAY, WHAT HO, FRY OLD BEAN

WHAT DO YOU KNOW... THE RECTOR HAS JUST GIVEN ME A SMALL TRUCK FOR HAVING THE BOGGLIEST EYES IN COLLEGE...

...HAVE YOU GOT ANYTHING YOU WANT TRANSPORTING ANYWHERE?

MNYAAH! CRUEL IRONY IS A FICKLE MISTRESS

STUDENT GRANT

MARCH 29th, THE FIRST DAY BACK AFTER THE CHRISTMAS VAC......

JIM BOWEN HALL

END OF TERM DISCO. FRIO...

WINNIE MANDELA HALL

HE-E-EY! GWAA-AANT! FIAT PANDA. NICE ONE. PWESSIE FWOM THE FOLKS?

YES...ERM...NO.

I... ERM... WON IT IN A CARD GAME ACTUALLY.

HEY GWEAT!

DID YOU CATCH THE CHWISTMAS THUNDERBIRDS?

NO. I DON'T WATCH TELEVISION. IT ROTS THE BRAIN ACTUALLY.

I SPENT THE WHOLE VAC PISSED OUT OF MY SKULL.

OOF.

I MET UP WITH SOME OF THE GUYS FROM THE SIXTH FORM ACTUALLY. WE WENT IN THE PUB AND DID THE BLOCKBUSTERS DANCE. GOD IT WAS FACKING HILARIOUS!

CHRIST. WE NEARLY GOT THROWN OUT. THE LANDLORD WAS CERTAINLY LOOKING AT US.

IT'S SAD REALLY- WE'RE GROWING APART. SOME OF THE GUYS ARE IN DEAD END JOBS, WITH MORTGAGES AND KIDS.

DINNERS WEEK 1.

THEY'VE NOT HAD THE CHANCE TO STAND ON THEIR OWN TWO FEET LIKE WE HAVE.

SHIT. MUM'S PUT THE WRONG YEAR ON THIS CHEQUE.

NEVER MIND GWAAANT. I GOT PWENTY OF CASH AT CHWISTMAS OFF MY FATH....ERM THAT I WON IN A CARD GAME. LET'S GO OUT FOR A FEW BEVVIES, EH?

OKAY THEN.

LIKE THE NEW LONG BWACK COAT. CHWISTMAS PWESSIE?

World of ...ats

NAH. OXFAM. FIVE PEE.

WOW. IT'S WEALLY WEALLY NICE.

World of Costly Coats

WEALLY LONG AND BWACK.

SPUNKBRIDGE UNIVERSITY GERRY ANDERSON BAR

GPD. SD. ST. I 99. VI 258.

HE-EY EVEWYONE! LOOK WHO'S HERE!!

HE-EY! IT'S GRANT!

CHRIST. WHAT A CRAPPOMUNDO VAC. I'VE JUST BEEN REVISING NON-STOP!

YOU GOT EXAMS THEN JAKE?

EVEWYONE'S GOT FACKING EXAMS GWANT.

YAH. AND I FOR ONE AM SHITTING BRICKS.

THE FIRST ONE'S TOMORROW MORNING.

FACK-OLA! I HAVEN'T DONE ANY REVISION!

..ERM... I MEAN, I DELIBERATELY HAVEN'T DONE ANY REVISION ACTUALLY.

WOW.

IT'S A PROTEST.

ERM...YEAH... I DON'T BELIEVE IN THE PRINCIPLE OF EXAMINATIONS. I DIDN'T COME TO SPUNKBRIDGE TO PASS STUPID TESTS OF SHORT-TERM MEMORY. I CAME HERE TO LEARN ABOUT LIFE.

4am NEXT MORNING...

JIM BOWEN HALL

AW SHIT AW SHIT I'M GOING TO FAIL.

I WANT MY MUMMY.

ROCK A BYE El

on the to
the pop

To millions of fans Elvis Presley was, and still is, (and always will be) quite simply The King. Of Rock 'n' Roll. And when he died, on the lavatory, wearing a nappy, in 1977, the whole world mourned the death of a star we had all come to know. And love.

But just how well *did* we know him? Not as well as we may have thought, according to a new book published this week. A book which takes an unusually intimate look at the private man behind the public face of Elvis Presley.

'Elvis – His Life and his Bedtime Routine' is a no-holds-barred biography which focuses on the end-of-day behavioural patterns of the man from Memphis who to many became the voice of rock'n'roll. Here, in a brief extract from the book, author Jimmy Hill, better known for his football analysis and big chin, gives us an insight into the lifestyle of a star; his supper times, his choice of late night viewing, his preferred bedtime drink. This, for the first time, is the *real* Elvis.

Adapted from the book
'ELVIS - HIS LIFE AND HIS BEDTIME ROUTINE'
by Jimmy Hill
Published by Honey Nut Loop Books at £19.95

'On 16th July 1977 Elvis Alan Presley set his bedside alarm clock for 8.30am, then pushed up the little knob that primed the bell to go off in the morning. Then he kicked off his slippers – first the right, then the left, and lay back his head on the pillow. Seconds later Elvis Presley was asleep.

ROUTINE

It was a routine that he had been through a thousand times before. But this time it was different. This time was the last time. For the next day, on 17th July 1977 Elvis Alan Presley was found dead, on the toilet.

GRACELANDS

Elvis' bedtime routine had been perfected over the many years during which he'd lived in his Gracelands mansion. In fact, in those latter years of his life, it was often said that neighbours could set their clocks by the time Elvis switched off his bedside lamp – 11.25pm exactly. But it hadn't always been like that.

As a youngster living in Tennessee, America, Elvis Alan Presley had often gone to bed early. His mother, Mrs Presley, had insisted that as a toddler the young Elvis should be in bed, teeth brushed and lights out, by 6.30pm. There, after a goodnight kiss from his mum, the young Elvis would lie awake and dream of becoming the King of rock'n'roll. By his side would be a little Teddy bear. A Teddy bear that would later be immortalised in the worlds of the song 'It's Now or Never'.

ADVENT

But all that was to change with the advent of World War Two, and Elvis' life and bedtime routine were turned upside down. Still in his teens, Elvis was drafted into the army and sent to fight in Germany. And army life came as quite a shock to the young boy from Tennessee, America. It wasn't only his haircut that changed. So did his sleeping habits too.

PIRELLI

Lights out in the army was 8.30pm sharp, though the young Private Presley would often stay awake reading by torchlight until nine o'clock. Or even ten o'clock if it was a good book. Sleeping conditions were cramped. Yet incredibly enough in the five years he spent in the army Elvis never once slept on the top bunk.

DUNLOP

After the war Elvis returned to America and had his first taste of success, topping the charts on both sides of the Atlantic with hits such as 'Hound Dog' and 'We're Caught In A Trap'. But with success came problems. Mrs

Presley still insisted that Elvis be in bed asleep by no later than 9.30. But Elvis, whose stage antics had earned him the nickname 'Pelvis', wanted to stay up late. Increasingly the rising star began to fall under the influence of Colonel Saunders, a mysterious figure who was later to manage his career.

GOODYEAR

The Colonel and Mrs Presley agreed a compromise whereby Elvis would have his supper and change into his pyjamas by 9.30. He was then allowed to watch TV until ten o'clock before going upstairs to the bathroom, brushing his teeth, washing his face and hands, and then going to bed.

GOODNESS

As during his army days, the King would occasionally read for a while before going to sleep. When he eventually became tired he would mark the page by folding back the top corner, then close the book and place it on his bedside table. *Remarkably, throughout his entire life Elvis never used a bookmark.*

A LIFE IN TOOTHBRUSHES

'Wise men say, only fools rush in'. And that was never more so the case than in the case of Elvis Alan Presley who never rushed in to a shop to buy a toothbrush. Incredible though it may seem, throughout his entire life the King of Rock'n'Roll never once bought a toothbrush for himself.

As a child his mother had always bought toothbrushes for him, possibly choosing red ones, as red was probably his favourite colour. In later life Elvis became less fussy about the colour of his toothbrushes, some of which would be bought by his mother, and others by his mentor Colonel Saunders.

MIDDLE

Occasionally, if Elvis was staying at a hotel and he'd forgotten his toothbrush, he would ring reception and ask if they'd got any toothbrushes. If they had some he'd ask for one, and if they didn't he'd maybe send someone out to a shop to buy one.

SIDE

In later years Elvis experimented with those bendy toothbrushes that

Young Elvis yesterday

can reach into difficult corners of your mouth, and at one stage an electric toothbrush was delivered to his mansion in Graceland, California. However, it was never used. For when, on 18th April 1980 Elvis Alan Presley was found dead, his electic toothbrush was found, still in its box, unopened, on a shelf nearby.

VIS
p of tree

Shortly before his death on the toilet Elvis was so fat (above) he could hardly fit into this photograph.

lvis (with fold through head) wants to play guitar, but mummy lvis (right) and Daddy Elvis (left) tell him 'It's time for bed'.

Eventually Elvis succumbed to the lure of Hollywood, and in 1969 he moved to Las Vegas. So began the Vegas years, an era when Mrs Presley's influence on her son began to wain. It is widely acknowledged that during these years Elvis began to drink beer, and take drugs, and this gradually began to take its toll on his bedtime routine.

SAKE

His bedtime got later and later. On several occasions he was still up and running about at eleven o'clock. He would watch films until yon time, sometimes drinking cocoa *after* he'd brushed his teeth.

HIPPY

He began to wear the same pyjamas for days on end without washing them, and then stopped wearing pyjamas at all. Instead he would sleep in the vest and underpants that he had been wearing all day. On one occasion it is rumoured that he even fell asleep in front of the television and awoke the next morning, never having been to bed at all.

For Elvis the end was in sight. Once a young man from Tennessee, America, Elvis Alan Presley had risen to the heady heights of the rock'n'roll tree. He had scaled the topmost pinnacle of rock, only to roll down the other side.

HIPPY

It is perhaps ironic that a man who spent so much of his life in bed, or about to get into it, and making preparations for getting into it, should not die in his bed. For Elvis once said to Colonel Saunders "Don't ever let me die in bed, Colonel Saunders".

SHAKE

And that dream came true. For on the 18th of April 1980 Elvis Alan Presley died. Not in a bed, but on the toilet. A sad but fitting end to a legend that will live forever. Even though he is dead, yet shall he live.

Elvis Alan Presley. Born 1955. Died 1980. Long live the king.

BLOCKBUSTER BOB'S FEET IN A MUDDLE

Bob Holness has come a long way since the sixties when he used to present some kids, TV programme or other in black and white.

But fans of the millionaire Blockbusters host are probably unaware that plucky Bob battled his way to the top of the telly tree despite a serious disability. For 44 year old Bob was born with his feet on the wrong legs. And getting his TV career off the ground was made almost impossible by the fact that his feet were the wrong way round.

WINDMILL

"It was very embarrassing at times", recalls Bob, whose luxury home is a £2 million converted windmill in the Lake District. "At school I would trip over and get myself into a muddle, and when I left I found it difficult to find work".

ICE HOUSE

Bob failed literally hundreds of TV auditions because of his condition. "Producers didn't want to know when I turned up for auditions with my feet on the wrong legs. They'd take one look and say 'Forget it'. I was turned down by Tomorrow's World, The Black and White Minstrel Show, Dr Who, Animal Magic and Grandstand – all in one afternoon".

SNOW CHAIN

Having your feet on the wrong legs can be an expensive business too. "Of course I could never buy a pair of shoes to fit me", recalls Bob. "Even today I have to buy two pairs of shoes, then throw half of them away".

But despite his age – Bob will be 67 this year – there are still no thoughts of retirement for Britain's favourite elderly kids' TV quiz show host.

SUN ROOF

However, at 67, telly veteran Bob may soon be hanging up his TV quiz boots. "I've been in this game for a long time, despite my unusual feet. And it may soon be time to call it a day, and make way for someone a little younger. And with their big toes on the inside".

But one thing is for sure. Bob won't be quitting his role as host of TV's Blockbusters. "You're as young as you feel, and I certainly don't feel like packing it all in yet. I never was one for gardening", said Bob yesterday.

FOG HORN

But Bob's retirement promises to be anything but relaxing. "I'm often busier at home than I am in the TV world", he admitted. And with two young kids, a hungry wife and a sizeable garden to look after, Bob will have his hands full.

Give us 'B' please Bob for Blockbuster's Bob Holness wearing a tie yesterday.

"One thing's for sure", quipped Bob yesterday. "I won't be sitting back and putting my unusual feet up for some time yet".

At the last count TV millionaire Holness was estimated to be worth £132 million.

Physical peculiarities of the brainy quiz show hosts

TV starter for ten brain box Bamber Gasgoine, arch telly rival of Blockbusting Bob Holness, had his ears on backwards for many years before undergoing corrective surgery for the problem.

HAIL CAESAR

ITV bosses used clever angles and mirrors to disguise swot Bamber's funny ears during filming of TV's University Challenge.

GALE TILSLEY

Ask The Family quiz host Robert Robinson has always refused corrective surgery on his peculiar eyes. Call My Bluff question master Robinson, one of the Beeb's brainiest quiz show hosts, was born with his eyes upside down.

Telly brainboxes Bamber 'G' (with hair) and Robert Robinson (without hair)

Lester Piggot's — Would you believe it... about... SUGAR

Sugar cane was brought to America by Colombus. The first plants were eaten... by imported goats!

See you next time fact fans!

23

QUEEN SCUTTLES FERGIE ON PORN VIDEO

Plans for a blockbusting ROYAL SEX VIDEO starring the Duchess of York have been TORPEDOED by the Queen.

'Fergie's Royal Guide To Having It Off' was set to earn the Duchess a staggering **£10 MILLION** through advance sales alone. But Fergie's plans were sunk yesterday when the Queen fired a Royal broadside, banning her daughter-in-law from appearing in the no holds barred steamy educational love film.

FORKED

If the video had gone ahead eager Royal watchers could have forked out £10.99 to see:

● **NUDE** Fergie rolling around on a mattress.

● **EXPLICIT** love acts between the Duchess and a male model.

● **OPEN** displays of masturbation techniques.

● and pop shots.

Production of the red hot video was already well underway when the Queen attached limpet mines to its hull, fearing that the publicity such a tape would attract could damage the public image of the Royals. And Palace insiders believe the Queen will have no hesitation in blasting similar projects out of the water with depth charges.

KNIFED

"The Queen would indeed frown upon any member of the Royal family participating in a videotape record-

Porky and Bess in a flap over flap shots

ing which features explicit sexual acts", a Buckingham Palace spokesman told us yesterday.

GARROTED

The Duchess is no stranger to the Queen's naval gunpower. Several crew

members were killed last year when an Exocet missile fired by the Queen struck Fergie aft of the poop deck after she had announced plans to appear naked in Penthouse magazine.

The Adventures of BILLY the FISH

WILL GILBERT O'SULLIVAN SAVE THE DAY FOR UNITED? OR WILL FULCHESTER STADIUM BURN – AND A RIVER OF BLOOD DROWN OUT THE CLUB'S CHAMPIONSHIP CHALLENGE? (LATEST ODDS ON THIS BEING THE LAST EVER BILLY THE FISH: 5-4)

HAVE NO FEAR! THE CAPTAIN'S HERE!

It's every fella's nightmare – visiting the newsagent to buy a dirty magazine. Well have no fear, because Captain Jazzmag is here to help horny readers who prefer not to buy their porny magazines over the counter.

DIRTY

For a modest £10 (to cover the price of the magazine, postage and our administration fee) Captain Jazzmag will pop over the road to our local newsagents and buy the dirty book of your choice, then post it to you under a plain cover.

PORNY

If you want to receive a porny magazine but would prefer not to buy it yourself, write to Captain Jazzmag at the address below. Fill in the form indicating the magazine your require, and don't forget to enclose ten pounds.

Dear Cap'n

I always wait until my local newsagent is empty before I go in and buy my jazz mag. But by the time I've plucked up the courage to take it to the till, there's always another customer has entered the shop. I'm on the verge of giving up. It's so frustrating. Please help me Captain Jazzmag. I enclose £10.

Brian
Hackney

CAPTAIN JAZZMAG says: Have no fear Captain Jazzmag is here! And here too is a copy of Razzle magazine, winging its way to you by first class post!

Dear Cap'n

I am totally besotted with the young girl who works behind the counter in my local newsagent, and the last thing I want is for her to know that I wank habitually. Please could you save the day, Captain Jazzmag, by sending me a copy of Escort in the post. I enclose £10.

Bob
Bolton

CAPTAIN JAZZMAG says: You're obviously a sensative fella, Bob. I'm only too pleased to be able to help. I'm sending you a copy and wish you wanking well!

Top shelf marks for newsagent

My big brother has lots of dirty books under his bed, but I haven't got any. I'm only 14 and the shopkeeper won't sell me any.
I don't think its fair. Please send me a dirty book. I enclose my pocket money – £10 exactly.

Richard
Hull

CAPTAIN JAZZMAG says: Top shelf marks to your local newsagent, Richard. He is quite right to say 'no'. At 14 the law says you are too young to buy a scud mag. Try flicking through your mum's clothes catalogues instead, in particular the underwear section.
I'm keeping your tenner to teach you a lesson, young man.
(P.S. Next time you write try saying you're 18.)

Dear Cap'n

I wouldn't dare buy a pornographic magazine in a shop, so I was going to subscribe to one. However, I don't want them to have my name and address on their computer, because you never know what they'll use it for. I'm at my wits end. Please help me Captain. I enclose £10.

George
Essex

CAPTAIN JAZZMAG says: I know how you feel, George. Subscribing direct to a jazzmag is a risky business. Not least of all because you can't be sure that they'll send it under plain cover.
You've done the right thing by writing to me. I'm sending you a sensational copy of Fiesta, in a plain brown envelope with an innocuous Newcastle postmark.

Dear Cap'n

I am a member of the cloth who likes the occasional hand shandy. But if I ventured into the newsagent in a close knit community, like Truro, I would be recognised and word of my 'off the wrist' activity would spread like wildfire.
I have prayed to the Lord for jazzmags, but none have appeared.
Please Captain Jazzmag, help me. You are my last hope. I enclose £10 from last Sunday's collection.

Rev. X
Cornwall

CAPTAIN JAZZMAG says: Shame on you! A man in your position should know better. People look up to you, and by spending their money on wank mags you betray their trust.
Is suggest you pray for forgiveness, and in the meantime I am keeping the ten pounds as punishment for your sins.

Dear Cap'n

I am only 4 feet 8 inches tall, and my local newsagent keeps all the male interest magazines on the top shelf, way out of my reach.
It is most embarrassing having to ask the assistant for a chair to stand on in order to reach them. Consequently I have not been able to get my hands on a porny magazine for over a year.
Please help by sending me a copy of Mayfair. I enclose £10.

Andy
Norfolk

CAPTAIN JAZZMAG says: That's a tall story Andy, but I can well believe it. Top shelf mags are often beyond the reach of little fellas like yourself. But don't worry. Soon you'll be able to reach new heights of enjoyment! This month's copy of Mayfair is on its way to you!

NAME_____ ADDRESS _____

_____

PLEASE SEND ME A COPY OF ☐ MAYFAIR ☐ RAZZLE
☐ PENTHOUSE ☐ PLAYBOY
☐ ANY WANK MAG (tick one)

I certify that I am aged 18 or over, and I enclose £10 cash.

Signed_____

Post to: Captain Jazzmag, Viz, P.O. Box 1PT, Newcastle upon Tyne, NE99 1PT

27

LETTERBOCKS

It wasn't me, honest

They say that we're all to blame for the increasing crime levels on our streets. Well I'm not. I was in the pub with me mates. Honest.

> J. Walsh
> Newbiggin

I reckon these TV Gladiators are as soft as shite. If they ever come down my local it won't be 'getting knocked of a podium with a pugil stick"; it would be 'getting knocked off a bar stool with a pool cue'. And no helmets, elbow pads or personal eye protectors either.

> M. Porteous
> Dudley

Congratulations to TV consumer programme 'Watchdog' on highlighting the dangers of these so-called breakfast snacks 'Pop Tarts'. Previously I had not realised that if I gave my child something to eat which had piping hot jam in the middle, burns may result. Perhaps now 'Watchdog' could turn their attention to evil coffee manufacturers. I have lost count of the number of times I have burnt my tongue by drinking coffee which is too hot. Clearly it is time that something was done about this problem too.

> B. Beaton
> Bogness

What about my piles?

Having just watched BBC's Blue Peter raise three quarters of a million pounds for Africans with bad eyesight, I was wondering how many of those Africans would like to hold a fund raising 'Bring and Buy' sale in aid of my haemorrhoids. Not fucking many I'll wager.

> J. Bowden
> Teignmouth

LetterBocks
P.O. Bocks 1PT
Newcastle upon Tyne
NE99 1PT

I sat through fifty minutes of Crimewatch UK the other night and I must say I didn't laugh once.

> D. Blair
> Twickenham

I spotted this amusing car registration number in a car park recently. Do I win £5?

> D. Wheeler
> Thornaby

I'm sure many of your readers share my concern about the lack of big brass bands in Britain. Come on Mr. Major! Get your thumb out, and let's put the 'oompah!' back in Britain.

> A. Chance
> Wimbledon

How about this one then?

> D. Wheeler
> Thornaby

I do have sympathy for the coal miners with all their current troubles. But let's be honest. If they'd dressed a bit smarter for work, and used a bar of soap every now and again, then people might be more inclined to give them their jobs back.

> A. Macclesfield
> Manchester

The King's Head

In days gone by public houses were named after our monarchs and their exploits, for example The Queen Victoria, The Kings Oak, etc. What a pity this is not done today – we'd have some great names, such as The Duchess And Slaphead, The Bent Prince, and The Prince of Wales' Bit on the Side.

> Norman Conquest
> Hastings

The King's dead

The sooner all these Elvis fans come to terms with the fact that their idol is dead, the sooner they'll begin to realise he was only a fat twat in the first place.

> J. Leonard
> Southpool

Esther Rantzen is always harping on about dogs that can say "sausages". Well, if I lie in the bath and fart I can make by bottom say "Edward Woodward". Do you think she'd be interested?

> A. Smith
> Anglesey

My hobby is playing word games with the names of pop stars. For instance, ABBA is a palindrome – it spells the same backwards. DOING JIGGY-JIGGY WITH MADONNA IN A BATH FULL OF SWARFEGA isn't a palindrome. I just like writing it down and thinking about it.

> Mick Dwyer
> Brighton

I'm fed up with these vegetarians who moan and bleat every time normal blokes like me go out and do a bit of hunting. If it wasn't for the likes of me the wildlife would eat all the lentils and sprouts and there'd be nothing left for the veggies. Then they'd all have to have sausages like everyone else.

> D. Bruce
> Colchester

As a New Year's resolution I decided not to smoke more than ten cigarettes a day. I thought I was doing really well until after a couple of weeks my wife pointed out that previously I had never smoked at all! I think there's a lesson here for us all.

> Peter Owners-Manual
> Haynes

I'm not impressed

Watching TV the other night I saw Rory Bremner doing impressions of Michael Hesletine, Bob Monkhouse and David Coleman. All well and good, Mr Bremner. But don't you have any talent of your own? These so called 'impressions' are just a waste of licence payers' money.

> P. Lloyd
> Port Sunlight

After following the gripping series of TV commercials for Gold Blend coffee, I tried popping round to my neighbour's flat to ask for a cup. After several attempts I am still nowhere near getting a cup of coffee, never mind a shag.

N. Stephens
Easington

Now there's a point

If Australia is so bloody great, why the fuck is there so many of them over here?

Colin Smith
Earls Court

It's unusual to see the mighty Liverpool lingering so near to the bottom of the Premier League this season, and a lot of critics are asking why. I'll tell you why. It's because they're *shite*.

K. Dixon
Manchester

My mother always used to say, "bottling things up never does anyone any good". Reflecting upon this a while later it occured to me that the local cider company seems to have done very well out of it, thank you very much.

Chris Hill
Somerset

In your Sausage Sandwich annual letters pages a Tom McArthur from Bolton asks for picture of a 'bird' to be printed, and for a picture of a bloke kissing the 'bird's' arse. Perhaps Mr. McArthur would like to send in a picture of some men with their little knobs out? Or better still, grow up and stop calling us birds. Alright?

Woman's Writes
Cheltenham

Any birds out there who *don't* mind being called birds please write to us. We are six good looking, big, muscular army plant operators with smart uniforms and we walk around with big guns looking dead hard. We're in Bosnia, and we'd appreciate letters and photos from any birds, age 20 upwards. Plus dirty pictures of course.

Pat, Woody, Scally, Robbo, Van & Will

● *Birds, get writing c/o: 24821905 Spr. Craine, Cmbt. Support Tp., 44 HQ & Sp. Sqn., 35 Engr. Regt., Op. Grapple T.S.G., BFPO 544.*

HOUSES GO TOPLESS

It's roofs off as temperatures soar!

The shape of things to come – a new 'open top' style house yesterday

Britain's building industry is heading for a revolution as climatic changes over the next few years look set to render roofs obsolete.

For centuries houses in Britain have traditionally been built with roofs on the top. But after one or two mild winters recently experts believe that weather patterns are changing, and soon houses will no longer need roofs as the country begins to bask in a new 'Mediterranean' style climate.

BURDEN

But while that may be good news for house owners who will no longer face the burden of expensive roof repairs, it's bad news for builders.

PRICE

"A lot of our work comes from building and repairing roofs on the top of houses", one builder told us yesterday. "If roofs go, then jobs will be lost. Many builders are already struggling in the recession, and I think no more roofs will be the last straw for a lot of them. Roofing companies especially are going to suffer".

VALENTINE

Yesterday the majority of builders we contacted reported that people were still asking for roofs on their houses. "We've just had an order for a house today, and they've asked for a slate roof on it", one told us. But influential architects are already believed to be designing houses without roofs, and if the mild weather continues a definite trend away from roofs is expected to emerge.

CHANDLER

There was, however, one good bit of news for builders. Almost all the houses in Britain today – *over 40,000 of them* – have already got roofs. And once demand for roofless property begins to increase, there should be several years work available removing the existing roofs.

TOP TIPS

CONVINCE friends you're filming a Channel 4 youth programme by taking your video camcorder to a party and whirling it around the most crowded room on the end of a piece of string.

V. James
Bow

FELLAS. Avoid pulling ugly birds. Simply drink 14 pints of beer and hey presto! Everyone you chat up looks like Catherine Zeta-Jones.

Paul & Scotty
BFPO 544 DRS

P.S. Make sure she's still a stunner the next morning by hiding a bottle of vodka under your pillow and drinking it before she wakes up. Hey presto! Breakfast with Cindy Crawford.

GARDENERS. Take a tip from fashion designers. Paint long, thin, parallel stripes on your garden hose to give the impression that it is longer than it actually is. Or paint thicker hoops along it's length to create a new, shorter look.

Percy Birke
Huddersfield

PRETEND you're listening to Radio One on Long Wave by slightly off tuning the FM frequency and wrapping the radio in a sleeping bag.

H. Clayton
Gateshead

UNDERWATER cameramen. Don't throw away those discarded supermarket trolleys. Tied together with string two of them make an ideal anti-shark cage.

Hapag Lloyd
Runcorn

TAXI drivers. Why not pop into a garage and ask them to fix your indicator lights for you so that other motorists know where the fuck you are going.

E. Murphy
Ipswich

FAT PEOPLE. Keep your hands warm in winter by unbuttoning your shirt and tucking them in between the layers of fat on your belly.

M. Jackson
Wolverhampton

STEREO too loud? Simply place the speakers inside a cupboard. The volume can then effectively be controlled by opening and closing the cupboard doors.

L. Shufflebottom
Market Drayton

DRINK drivers. Before motoring home after an evening on the piss, try sucking on an extra strong mint. Later, when police stop you for swerving across the road and driving on the pavement, they'll never in a million years suspect that you've been drinking.

R. Luck
HM Prison Shotts

ANTIQUE dealers. Calculate the age of old tables by sawing off one of the legs and counting the number of rings in the woodgrain. This works for chairs too.

A. Sapling
Sevenoaks

GIVE your goldfish a love-bite by inserting a straw into its bowl and sucking gently at its neck.

W. B. Levit
Hull

29

ROYAL HOAXOS
'Dinosaurs di
reveals book on Royals

Dinosaurs, the huge reptiles popularly believed to have roamed the earth millions of years ago, never existed – according to claims being made in a new book about the Royal Family.

And if the claim is proved to be true it will leave red-faced film maker Steven Spielberg facing financial disaster. For the man behind the blockbusting movie 'Jurassic Park' is sure to face a bill for **BILLIONS** of dollars from angry cinema goers demanding their money back.

COMPENSATION

But ironically Spielberg's American lawyers could turn to the British Royal Family for compensation. For a book published this week reveals that dinosaurs were an elaborate hoax, dreampt up by Queen Victoria.

DAMAGES

In his astonishing book 'True Stories About The Royals', wallpaper hanger Clive Bagshaw reveals how, in the olden days, Queen Victoria got together with black and white comedian Charlie Chaplin and set about dumbfounding animal experts by burying huge bones at various sites throughout the world in order to fool people into thinking there had been dinosaurs.

MAINTENANCE

The 'bones', paid for by Queen Victoria and hand carved out of wood by her personal carpenters, were then handed over to Chaplin for burial. The comic, famous for his moustache, hat and not saying anything, buried the bones over a period of many years, using a shovel.

"It all began as a joke", says author Clive, who found out about the scam after meeting a retired carpenter in a pub near Birmingham. "But when the first dinosaur bones were discovered at Lym Regis in the late nineteenth century, people took them seriously".

ALIMONY

Even Charles Darwin, the leading zoologist of the day, was hoodwinked. And he included dinosaurs in his Theory Of Evolution. Dinosaur remains were uncovered all over the world, and skeletons were painstakingly reassembled to reveal the giant lizard shapes we have all come to recognise.

COSTS

"The funny thing is that the experts got it all wrong", says Clive. "Queen Victoria designed the Brontosaurus, for example, with a short neck and a very, very long tail. But when they put the bones together they put half the tail on the neck, making them both quite long. And the Tyranosaurus wasn't supposed to have a tail at all. It was supposed to have a big long right arm, for punching other dinosaurs with".

EXPENSES

These dramatic revelations are sure to cause embarrassment among animal experts, many of whom have staked their reputations on dinosaurs having once ruled the Earth. When we rang top animal expert

David Attenborough, who actually played himself in the film 'Jurassic Park', he appeared stunned by the news.

"You're kidding", he said at first. "I'm going to look a right twat when this comes out. Are you sure there hasn't been a mistake?" Attenborough then told us he needed some time to think, and hung up.

FEE

Outside a London cinema where the film 'Jurassic Park' is continuing its record-breaking run, shocked members of the public began to demand a refund

David Attenborough - 'I'm going to look a right twat'.

when they heard news of the hoax. "I've paid £5 to see a film about dinosaurs only to find that they didn't even exist", one disappointed movie goer told us. As news of the hoax spread around the cinema scuffles broke out at the box office and eventually the police were called.

BUNG

Meanwhile, a spokesman for Buckingham Palace responded cautiously to the allegation that Queen Victoria was to blame for the controversy. "If what you say is true, and we do not necessarily accept that it

A brontosaurus as Queen Victoria had originally designed it, with a very, very long tail, and no neck whatsoever.

KINGS OF CRIME

It is now almost common knowledge that Prince Charles, the Prince of Wales, was the notorious 'Jack the Ripper'. We have all heard how, during the evenings, our future King terrorised Victorian London by stalking prostitutes in the fog, and butchering them with surgical instruments.

But how many people are aware that his father Prince Phillip organised the Great Train Robbery? Or that Princess Margaret was once caught on video robbing a sub post office of £8,000?

LIGHT

These are just some of the startling Royal crime revelations that are set to come to light in Clive Bagshaw's fascinating new book. And it also details the elaborate measures taken by the Government to cover up Royal crime.

HEAVY

Prince Phillip, the book alleges, was the mastermind behind Britain's most famous robbery. In 1964 Phillip, who had yet to meet the Queen, had just arrived in Britain from Greece. He met up with London underworld

villains Reggie Biggs and Roger Daltrey, and together they masterminded the Royal Mail robbery.

Book reveals rogues' gallery of Royals

"It was in fact Prince Phillip who coshed the train driver, causing him permanent injuries", Clive revealed. The gang made off with a total haul of over £2 million in stamps and postal orders. "Ironically, it was while Phillip was counting out his share of the loot that he fell in love with the Queen after seeing her face over and over again on stolen stamps. He met her at a party a few weeks later, and they were married at Westminster Abbey".

Princess Margaret's crimes have been small compared to her brother Phillip's. "She has a record as long as your arm, mostly for petty crimes. Shoplifting, car theft and house breaking. But every time she's arrested the Royal Protection Squad swing into action, and her files are conveniently lost or destroyed", Clive told us.

BANTAM

But the tab loving Princess almost blew it the day she held up a sub post office in Dudley. Armed with a

URUS! n't exist'

Dinosaur conspirators Queen Victoria and Charlie Chaplin, (Chaplin is on the right, with the more prominent moustache)

is, then surely Mr Chaplin is more directly to blame than Queen Victoria, because it was he who actually buried the bones".

Chaplin was yesterday unavailable for comment, having died several years ago at his home in Switzerland. However, his widow, Mrs Chaplin, could soon be on the receiving end of some pretty angry phone calls.

Prince Philip, Princess Madge and the Queen Mum (who, at the time this picture was taken, looked noticeably alive).

realistic imitation firearm, she forced terrified staff to hand over £8,000 cash before escaping on a stolen moped. But video evidence of the hold-up was sent to the BBC's 'Crimewatch' programme in the hope that TV viewers could identify the culprit.

Seconds before the video footage was screened on nationwide TV a BBC technician recognised the Princess's distinctive crown. BBC chiefs immediately pulled the plug on the broadcast, and called in Royal Protection Squad officers. When confronted, the Princess confessed to the crime and handed over the missing money. Beyond that no police action was taken.

Other allegations made in the book include the suggestion that the Kray twins were framed for the murder of Jack 'The Hat' McVitie to get Her Majesty The Queen Mother off the hook.

ROAD ISLAND

TV comic and 'Eastenders' star Mike Reid yesterday pleaded for the Krays to be released as soon as possible. "They never did anyone any harm, apart from killing people. What kind of justice do we have when joy riders walk away from the courts scott free, while a couple of nice East End blokes who never harmed a fly go to prison for something as trivial as a couple of gangland murders?"

HORROR STAR'S DEATH SHOCKS POTATO MARKET

The tragic death of Hollywood horror star Vincent Price has not only rocked the acting profession, it has also hit the price of potatoes.

And Price's unfortunate death at the age of 82 could put as much as a penny on the price of a packet of crisps.

HAMMER

For unknown to his many fans Price, the star of numerous Hammer horror films, was the world's greatest collector of potatoes.

BELL

Throughout his career the accomplished actor whose distinctive voice was heard on Michael Jackson's 'Thriller', spent practically all his earnings on potatoes, hoarding them in vast quantities in warehouses all over Britain and the United States. And according to one vegetable expert, Price was no fool when it came to buying potatoes.

Lawyers in dash for mash stash

"Vincent would always buy potatoes cheap. Whenever the price slumped for any reason, he'd be in, buying up huge stocks at rock bottom prices. Heaven knows where he put them, but he'd buy literally tons at a time. And he always paid in cash".

SONG

The mystery of the whereabouts of Price's potato hoards is now set to baffle top Hollywood lawyers as they set about the task of carving up the actor's estate. For although the star left little cash, he is believed to own as many as a *trillion* potatoes, although their whereabouts remains a mystery. For the shrewd actor kept no records of his potato purchases, and no paperwork appears to exist detailing their whereabouts.

SUNG

Meanwhile, the value of shares in crisps fell dramatically as dealers anticipated a flood of cheap potatoes being released onto the market. And crisp manufacturers look set to respond by raising the price of crisps to the consumer, thus bolstering flagging profits.

BLUE

However the mystery of Price's missing potatoes remains unsolved. And fellow actor Anthony Hopkins was yesterday unable to cast any light on the spuds' whereabouts. "I didn't know that Vincent collected potatoes", he told us.

Dana's formula for success

Irish pop Queen Dana is set to take a leaf out of Paul Newman's book by starting her own motor racing team.

Formula One fan Dana, who sprang to fame twenty years ago as a winner in the Eurovision Song Contest, plans to be up and racing with her 'Team Dana' in time for the start of the next Formula One racing season. And the ambitious songbird is setting her sights high, with plans to lift the coveted World Formula One Grand Prix Championship in her first season.

EVERY

Dana is putting her money where her mouth is, pumping royalties from radio plays of her hit 'All Kinds of Everything' into the racing venture. But she is thought to be well short of the **millions** of pounds required to buy a car, and put a successful racing team together. And as one race insider revealed, her plans to raise sponsorship have hit a snag.

BODY

"Dana is insisting that she drive her own car. She refuses to let anyone else do it. And that is proving to be a major hurdle in attracting big money sponsorship"

KNOWS

Following her spectacular Eurovision success Dana's career was put on hold by a double blow. First she required hospital treatment for throat problems affecting her voice. Then a West

Dana and her car yesterday.

End musical which she had written and produced bombed, leaving the singer penniless.

ONE

'Louder Lauda' was based on the life story of Formula One racing hero Nicky Lauda, and starred Dana in the title role. Critics slammed her portrayal of the former world champion driver as 'shambolic', and the show closed down after only three nights.

THEY LOVE IT REALLY

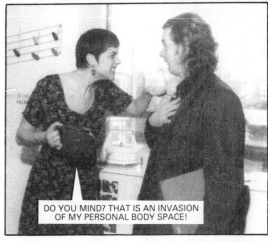

Hard working and efficient secretary Cathy Carruthers was good at her job in a busy city centre office. However, the guys in the office appreciated her other qualities.

Photography by Colin Davison. We have been asked to point out that the principle model taking part in this photo story was unaware of the precise content of the script.

38

THE END

IT SEEMED LIKE AN INNOCENT DAY OUT. LITTLE DID THE HAPPY, SINGING ROBINSON FAMILY KNOW THAT THEIR CAR FILLED WITH ALL THE TRAPPINGS OF A PICNIC IN THE COUNTRYSIDE WAS ON A...

ONE WAY TRIP TO HELL

THERE MUST HAVE BEEN AN ACCIDENT. WE'RE BEING FLAGGED DOWN.

I AM AN ARMED OFFICER OF THE OFFICE OF BOTTOM INSPECTION. THROW OUT YOUR KEYS.

SLOWLY EXIT THE VEHICLE KEEPING YOUR HANDS AWAY FROM YOUR BOTTOMS AT ALL TIMES.

DO IT!

YOUR PAPERS PLEASE.

I THINK YOU'LL FIND EVERYTHING IN ORDER.

WE SHALL SEE.

YOUR CONFIDENCE IS ILL-FOUNDED. THIS ROLL HAS BEEN BADLY RE-SPOOLED AFTER OVER-ENTHUSIASTIC PULLING... A MINOR CRIME IN ITSELF...

BUT THE PERFORATIONS - THEY DIDN'T TEAR...

SILENCE!

ACCORDING TO OUR RECORDS THIS ROLL WAS ISSUED EIGHT DAYS AGO...

YET YOU SEEM TO HAVE USED A DIS-PROPORTIONATE NUMBER OF SHEETS.

REMOVE YOUR LOWER GARMENTS AND **BARE YOUR BOTTOMS!** THE INSPECTION PROPER IS ABOUT TO BEGIN.

STOP! CORPRAL, NOTE HOW THIS MAN'S UNDERPANTS HAVE RIDDEN UP INTO HIS BUM-CRACK DUE TO FAILURE OF THE LEG-HOLE RETAINING ELASTIC... *HUNGRY ARSE* IS A SERIOUS CRIME, MR. ROBINSON. YOU'RE LOOKING AT TEN YEARS AND YOU HAVEN'T EVEN GOT YOUR KEX OFF YET.

YOU HAVE BEEN SITTING ON A SEAT-COVER MADE FROM WOODEN BALLS MR. ROBINSON, LEAVING A PATTERN OF SMALL ROUND INDENTATIONS IN THE FLESH OF YOUR BUTTOCKS ... A FURTHER FIVE YEARS - FOR *GOLF BALL ARSE!*

TAKE ME INSTEAD. I HAVE NO FAMILY TO SUPPORT. I'M OLD, MY BEST YEARS ARE PAST.

TAKE HIM AWAY!

NO UNCLE ALBERT!

VERY MOVING... BUT THERE IS NO QUESTION OF US TAKING YOU INSTEAD, YOU'D NOT SURVIVE THE JOURNEY... WE'RE TAKING YOU *AS WELL!*

HA! HA! HA!

BUT WHAT'S THE CHARGE YOU FIEND?

SIMPLE... YOUR RINGPIECE IS *TOO HAIRY!*

BUT SURELY THAT'S NOT A CRIME.

TRUE... NOT IN ITSELF.

BUT THE HAIR IS GINGER.

OH GOD... THEY'VE GOT ME.

ENJOY YOUR FART EARLIER SONNY?

THESE ARE YOUR UNDERPANTS MASTER ROBINSON?

I HAVEN'T FARTED... YOU CAN'T PROVE IT.

YES.

WELL, THEY TELL A DIFFERENT STORY... YOU'VE FOLLOWED THROUGH.

GASP!

NOW... MRS. ROBINSON, YOU HAVE A VERY LOVELY BOTTOM ... NOTHING ASTRAY HERE...

CLEAN, NEAT, SWEET-SMELLING ...NOTHING AT ALL WRONG WITH YOUR BOTTOM.

SUPER. DOES THAT MEAN I CAN GO?

HA! HA! HA! BUT THAT IT DID MRS. ROBINSON... THERE ARE RED ELBOW MARKS JUST ABOVE YOUR KNEES ... AS YOU KNOW, READING ON THE TOILET AFTER THE LAST STOOL HAS BEEN PASSED IS A *HANGING OFFENCE!*

CHOP! CHOP! CHOP!

HA HA! HA HA!

NEXT EPISODE: *PRISONER CELL BLOCK ARSE*

40

BUCKS LOSE THEIR FIZZ OVER EURO-TUNNEL

Eurovision song contest winners Bucks Fizz have fallen out — after failing to 'make their minds up' over plans for a new Channel Tunnel.

The band topped the charts throughout the early eighties after their celebrated Euro-victory. But plans to build a new Channel Tunnel, in direct opposition to the 'Chunnel' rail link, proved to be their undoing. And now the four members have parted company after falling out over the ambitious tunnel scheme.

PLOUGH

Jay Aston, Cheryl Baker, Bobby Gee and Mike Nolan had decided to plough the profits from hits such as 'My Cam-er-ra N-ever Lies' into a 400 mile tunnel beneath the sea bed, stretching from Whitby in North Yorkshire to the Danish port of Esjberg. With backing from their record company the group had planned to have the new cross channel route completed by June this year.

BLACK BULL

However, they soon faced a major technical setback when plans to use a 'Thunderbirds' style mechanical mole to dig the tunnel had to be scrapped. Fearing that conventional tunnelling techniques would prove too expensive, Cheryl Baker withdrew from the project,

Baker – dropped out

Pop tunnel project goes FLAT!

leaving the other three members divided as to whether to carry on.

KINGS HEAD

"Bobby Gee was determined to go ahead, but Mike Nolan wanted to take a shorter route – to Holland or Belgium", an insider told us. "Meanwhile Jay refused to co-operate unless she was allowed to draw the plans".

RED LION

Nevertheless, the project seemed to be back on the rails in 1992 when Bobby and Mike reached a compromise, and it looked as if a Bucks Fizz channel tunnel was definitely on the cards, from Whitby to Bremerhaven in North Germany. Work was due to commence on the project early this year. But all that had to be cancelled when Aston dramatically quit the group after a row over how wide the tunnel should be.

WHEATSHEAF

Now the project has been shelved indefinitely, and the four former group members are embroiled in a bitter mud slinging match, each blaming the others for the tunnel's collapse.

ANCHOR

A solicitor speaking on behalf of Jay Aston yesterday issued the following brief statement. "I can confirm that Jay Aston no longer has any involvement in Bucks Fizz's plans to build a channel tunnel, and she is at present considering legal action against the other members of the group

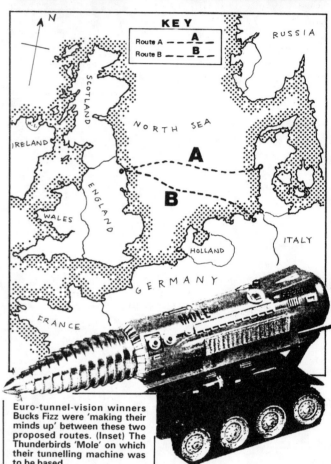

Euro-tunnel-vision winners Bucks Fizz were 'making their minds up' between these two proposed routes. (Inset) The Thunderbirds 'Mole' on which their tunnelling machine was to be based.

whose mismanagement of the project she feels led to its inevitable abandonment. Under the circumstances any further comment would be inappropriate".

KERRYGOLD

At the time of going to press no other members of the group were available for comment.

LURPACK

In 1985 a similar project ended in acrimony after EMI Records took court action to prevent Guys And Dolls from launching a cut price ferry service from Swanage in Dorset to Dieppe on the coast of France.

IT'S BAD MANNERS READING AT THE TABLE.

Joke

LIP-UP FATTY, FATTY LIP-UP FATTY, FATTY REGGAE!

IT'S FRIDAY...IT'S FIVE TO FIVE...IT'S...
THEORETICAL PHYSICS!

What have the following TV stars all got in common? Michael Aspel, Bernie Clifton, Leslie Crowther, Ed Stewart and the late Eammon Andrews.

If you said they were all presenters of the popular kids' programme Crackerjack you would of course be right. But there is another less obvious link. For believe it or not each of them has at some time in the past baffled the scientific world with their own controversial and at times incredible physics theory.

SECRETS

The physics theories of the Crackerjack presenters has for many years been one of TV's best kept secrets. But now, for the first time, using files only just released from the BBC archives, we can exclusively reveal the physics theories of the former Crackerjack stars.

SCIENCE

MICHAEL ASPEL – launched a hugely successful career in TV with his appearances on Crackerjack in the early seventies. Since then he has never looked back, and is now one of Britain's top TV earners. But Michael's first love was always science, and in 1972 he published his own theory.

BOX

Aspel's theory was, quite simply, that if you spin around inside a box, you get dizzy. But if the box is then raised to 100 feet above ground level, and you spin around in it, you *don't* get dizzy.

GENIUS

This remarkable discovery was published in all the major scientific journals of the day, and Aspel was heralded as a genius by many experts. But the theory was disproved a short while later when a man spinning round inside a box 100 feet above the ground got dizzy. When the box was lowered to the ground the man got out and fell over.

EXCLUSIVE

Crackerjack stars (left to right) Glaze, Crowther, Aspel, Don McLean and a bird

Crazy double lives of the TV Crackerjack boffins

Aspel was devastated. He immediately cancelled all his research and concentrated instead on his TV career. Needless to say he hasn't looked back since.

OSTRICH

BERNIE CLIFTON – is known to millions of kids as the man with the comedy ostrich. But during the seventies he starred as Crackerjack's resident funny man, and also took time out to develop a physics theory of his own.

EXPRESS

Bernie's belief was and still is that if you run backwards along the top of an express train which is travelling forwards at 100 miles per hour, the hands on your watch will move backwards.

FILTER

The Clifton Theory, as it became known, broke new ground for physics theoreticists. For he was challenging the very concept of time itself. And although his theory has never been substantiated by a successful controlled experiment, Clifton still has his supporters in the science world, among them the old bloke off 'How'.

CAPPUCINO

Physics theories of the Crackerjack presenters range from the brilliant to the bizarre. For instance **STU FRANCIS** once told delegates at a science conference

in Bridlington 'If you wee into a milk bottle in a green house wearing a tin foil hat on your head, the temperature of your head will be equal to the volume of wee in the bottle, divided by its weight'.

INSTANT

And it was former presenter **ED STEWART** who made headlines in 1974 when he claimed that 'The total weight of apples on any tree would be sufficient to lift the tree out of the ground if gravity was upside down'.

APPLE

LESLIE CROWTHER, who played funny man to Peter Glaze's straight man on the show, added his own apple theory when he said that 'The number of apples on any number of apple trees at any one time is equal to that number of trees divided by itself, and multiplied by the total number of apples thereupon'. Crowther's Theory of Apples on Trees has since become universally accepted and is used by apple growers worldwide when calculating how many apples they have on their trees.

EMI

A BBC book entitled 'Unusual Physics Theories of the Former Crackerjack Stars' is due to be published later this month by BBC Publications, priced £14.99.

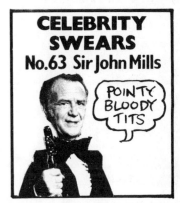

CELEBRITY SWEARS No.63 Sir John Mills

POINTY BLOODY TITS

BATTLE OF THE BONDS

A war of words is raging between former James Bond stars over the unlikely issue of garden conservatories. And the script for this real life Bond epic is set to make the movies look tame by comparison.

Trouble flared when former Bond No.1 Sean Connery had a £2,000 uPVC conservatory built at a house he owns in Scotland. Nothing unusual about that, you'd have thought.

GREENHOUSE

Enter Bond No. 2 George Lazenby, and immediately sparks begin to fly. "That's not a conservatory – it's a greenhouse", claimed the Aussie born star of On Her Majesty's Secret Service, when we showed him pictures of the building.

PORCH

To make matters worse a third Bond, Roger Moore, failed to agree with either of his 007 predecessors. "I think it's a porch", commented the 62 year old star. "I'd say that any glazed structure which encloses a main entrance to a building is, by definition, a porch", added the former 'Saint' actor and Britain's first TV millionaire.

LEAN-TO

Connery, for many the greatest Bond of all, is said to be furious that his successors to the role created by author Ian Fleming have been so quick to condem his lean-to glazed structure, although he prefered not to comment when we called him yesterday. But close friends of the millionaire actor, banker and golf course owner admitted he had been "purple with rage" to hear his conservatory described as a 'porch' by another former Bond.

ARCHITECT

"It's a grey area, one leading architect told us yesterday. "There is no concise definition of what does and what does not constitute a conservatory.

BUILDER

If a former Bond star pays a builder to build a conservatory, then providing he is himself happy with the structure, it can by his own definition be a conservatory. The opinions of his colleagues should not concern him".

Bonds throw stones over glass houses

Dalton – 'Matter of usage'

A conservatory similar to that of Connery's

Connery – Conservatory crisis

We rang current Bond star Timothy Dalton and asked him where he stood on the issue. "I'd say that it's a matter of usage", he told us. "If a structure exists merely to protect an entrance and prevent draughts etc., then it is a porch. If however it contains seating, flowers etc. it clearly has a separate function and becomes a conservatory", he told us.

But the case wasn't closed. Dalton rang us back ten minutes later. "I've been thinking", he said. "A porch would not necessarily have a glazed roof, whilst a conservatory would", he told us. "And we can easily distinguish between a conservatory and a greenhouse, as a greenhouse must be erected for the sole purpose of plant propagation", he added.

Double O-pinion

Rodney – 00 Plonker

Meldrew – 00 Misery

Catherine – 00 Darling Bud

We wondered who the next James Bond might be, and what *they* would make of the great conservatory debate.

'Plonker' Rodney, alias TV's Nicholas Lyndhurst told us he'd be honoured if the role of James Bond was ever offered to him. But he wasn't so sure about conservatories. "I've often visited an 'orangery' in Regent's Park, and that seems like nothing more than a conservatory to me. It's difficult isn't it?", he told us.

We thought TV grump Victor Meldrew, alias po-faced actor Richard Wilson, would make an interesting choice as the next Bond. "I don't know that I'm not a bit too old for the part", he told us in his unmistakable grumpy voice. Meldrew's definition of a conservatory was just as unenthusiastic. "I suppose it would have to have some flowers in it or something", said Britain's favourite TV misery.

Darling Bud Catherine Zeta Jones admitted that she had never dreampt of playing Bond. "I'm a woman, and James Bond is really a man's role", she told us. But the glamorous starlet turned pop singer had no hesitation in defining the difference between a conservatory and a greenhouse. "Surely a greenhouse would be a free standing structure, whilst a conservatory would be attached, to, and accessible from a house", she said.

HOLLYWOOD STARS TO GIVE BIRTH TO ENDANGERED SPECIES

Top scientists believe they have solved the genetic riddle that will enable Hollywood Stars to give birth to animal babies.

After a dramatic breakthrough by researchers at the University of California it appears that American Scientists have reached the summit of the mountain on top of which lies the final piece of jigsaw required to complete the genetic crossword puzzle that has baffled man throughout the centuries – the key to the very Rubik's Cube of life itself.

DNA

Scientists have discovered a method of injecting animal DNA – a sort of biological barcode which is printed on the bottom of all living things – into eggs taken from human ovaries – turning a woman's baby into the animal of her choice.

KLF

And conservationists are hopeful that if tests prove successful, within weeks women could be giving birth to endangered species of animals such as panda bears, tigers and snow leopards.

EMF

Already a host of Hollywood stars a queuing up to receive injections of animal DNA. And top of the list is thought to be Jane Fonda.

In private she has vowed to friends that she will personally have four pandas a year until the species is safe from the threat of extinction. And fellow Scot Sheena Easton has vowed to have at least one buffalo.

ELO

One of the advantages of this new breakthrough in genetic engineering is that Hollywood stars will be able to have the animal baby of their choice – without actually having to go to bed with that kind of ani-

By our Science Correspondent LULU

mal. Unless of course they particularly want to.

Instead human eggs will be removed from the ovary, boiled for two minutes, and then DNA from the chosen animal will be injected into a small hole drilled in the shell.

The egg will then be replaced by surgeons, and a few months later the woman will give birth to a baby animal.

ELP

The exact length of the pregnancy – the gestation period – will probably depend on how long it usually takes that sort of animal to have a baby, multiplied by how long a human takes. Or something like that.

BCRs

It was this same remarkable scientific breakthrough that Stephen Spielberg used as the basis for his blockbuster film Jurassic Park in which previously extinct dinosaurs are recreated by injecting traces of their DNA – found on pine cones – into crocodile eggs.

VCRs

However, it was felt that Hollywood stars such as Elizabeth Taylor, Michelle Pfeiffer, Kim Basinger and Sharon Stone would be reluctant to give birth to anything as large and awkwardly shaped as a dinosaur.

Big screen sex sirens could soon have "animal babies"

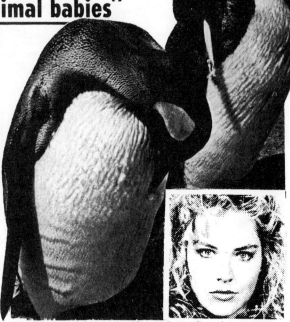

TAYLOR: 'No' to dinosaur delivery

"That would be like trying to get a JCB digger through a car tyre", one leading gyneacologist told us yesterday.

JCBs

But this week as Hollywood's first $25,000 per day animal baby clinic opened its's doors to the stars, there were fears that moral and ethical considerations were being overlooked, and that animal babies could simply become the latest fashion accessory in Tinseltown.

HGVs

Some commentators fear that fickle celebrities will tire of having tigers and that genetic cross-breeding could become fashionable, with stars like Julia Roberts possibly mixing pig, sausage dog and elephant DNA in order to have a pink baby elephant with short legs and a long body.

PSVs

But the Californian scientists working on the project

'Look! No nickers' star Sharon Stone (inset) could soon be p-p-p-picking up a penguin pregnancy at a Hollywood animal baby clinic. And examples of the endangered birds could soon be joining her much admired muff - up her skirt.

have no such fears. "In two, perhaps three months time, anything will be possible. For example, by taking samples of DNA from the late Charlie Chaplin's hat or John Wayne's trousers and injecting them into the eggs of, for example, a snake, we could breed a tall snake with a moustache that could ride a horse, but that wasn't very funny", one scientist told us yesterday.

WEMBLEY DATE FOR THE STARS

A galaxy of big name stars from the world of pop have lined up a spectacular gala charity concert at Wembley Stadium in October.

Top acts including Phil Collins, U2, Sting, INXS, Elton John, George Michael and Guns 'N' Roses are being lined up to perform , and messages of support have already been received from Paul McCartney and Michael Jackson. A charity single featuring all the participating artists will be released for Christmas.

RAISE

The stars taking part in the spectacular event hope to raise millions of pounds, although they haven't decided what for yet. "So far the support we've received has been magnificent", one told us yesterday. "Everybody we've spoken to has immediately dropped what they were doing and offered help. People have

Big names line up for charity show

been pulling out all the stops, and we're sure that this thing is going to be a massive success".

(al)READY

However, plans for the concert have already been criticised by one controversial pop figure - outspoken pop bendy gob and veteran toss pot Jonathon King. "I don't know what this event is in aid of, but whatever it is I'll be fundamentally opposed to it', he said speaking out of his bendy gob yesterday.

An American scientist at the forefront of genetic engineering research prepares to inject a human egg with mongoose DNA

THE SID THE SEXIST

6:30am SUNDAY...

REET. HERE'S THE WANK LINES.

GOOD MORNING SIDNEY, I'VE MADE YOU A CUP OF TEA. BY THE WAY, THE PHONE IS INCOMING CALLS ONLY SINCE THAT LAST BILL..

!?

IT'S YOU RINGING YOUR FRIENDS AT ALL HOURS WHEN I'M ASLEEP...

PHONE BILL

...WHERE IS 0898 THE CODE FOR ANYWAY?

ERM...

12 NOON, IN THE PUB...

HOW BAZ MAN... I WURK UP THIS MORNIN' IN KIP WI' BLONDE TRIPLETS... THERE WAS THREE O' THEM Y'KNAA...

...HEY, I COULDN'T BELIEVE HOW MUCH SEX THEY WERE GIVIN' US AN' THAT.

I CANNAT EVEN REMEMBER WHERE I PULLED THEM 'COZ I DRANK THAT MUCH AN' THAT.

hmmm...

HEY MAN, I SAW THEIR TITS AN' EVERYTHINK.

FUCK!?! BAZ! WHAT'S WRANG WI' YU? YER READIN' THE FUCKIN' SUNDAY TIMES, WHAT'S GANNIN' ON?! THEZ NAE KNOCKAZ IN IT MAN! IT'S AAL BIG WAARDS AN' NAE PIKSHAZ!

SID MAN, YORROOT O' TOUCH. THIS PAPER IS CHOCCA WI' HIGH QUALITY FLUFF.

HEY MAN, THEZ AALWEZ AN' AN ARTICLE ABOOT MADONNA WI' PIKSHAZ OF 'ER FEELIN' 'ER TWAT.

LURDS O' TOTTIE MAN SID, AAL DRESSED UP AS FASHION.

BUT BAZ, Y'DIVVENT GET THE REAL NEWS...

...ABOOT SEX VICARS AN' SURP STARS AN' THAT.

AN' THEZ NAE PIKSHAZ O' CATHERINE ZETA JURNZ IN TIGHT TROOZAZ AN' THAT.

YE MIGHT BE IN THERE, NOW SHE'S HAD THE PUSH OFF THAT BIG LANG DRINK O' WATTA OFF BLUE PETER.

EEH, LOOK AT THIS BAZ, ADVORTS FOR MASSAGE PARLAR.

AYE, THEZ LASSES IN THEM WHAT'LL PULL Y'OFF FORRA FIVER.

APPARENTLY.

DISGUSTIN.

AYE. Y'STICK A FIVER IN YER SHREDDIES, THAT'S THE SIGNAL, SEE SID.

WELL, THE DAY I PAY FORRIT IS THE DAY I STOP DEEIN' IT.

15 MINUTES LATER...

MASSAGE

THE PINK OBOE MASSAGE PARLOUR

ASSISTED SHOWER £30
FRENCH £25
FULL BODY MASSAGE £35
CHOCOLATE SANDWICH £50
MAYONAISE ON BROWN £15 (CRUSHED NUTS 50p EXTRA)
STICKY-BELLY FLAP-COCK £10
APRICOT SUNDAE £8
STANDARD WANK £5

INSIDE...

HOW PET... I'VE COME FORRA BIT RUB-DOWN AN' THAT... NUDE... Y'KNAA... RUB-DOWN... Y'KNAA...

YES... WELL, WHY DON'T YOU STEP INTO OUR SOLARIUM, POP ON YOUR GOGGLES AND SANDY WILL JOIN YOU PRESENTLY.

...A PERSONAL MASSAGE... 'COZ I'M A BIT STIFF Y'SEE... MIND YE, I DIVVENT HAVE TU DEE THIS...

I CAN PULL OWT, ME.

SO... HEH! HEH! HEH! THIS IS GANNA BE MAGIC! I HERP THIS SANDY BORD'S A LOOKA. EEEH, MIND Y'CANNAT SEE A BLOODY THING WI' THESE STUPIT GEPS ON.

mmmmh...oooh... Sandy... yes! yes!

TUG! TUG! TUG! TUG! TUG! TUG!

DID YOU ENJOY THAT YOUNG MAN?

huh!?

SANDY

AAAAIEEEE!!

NEXT DAY...

HOW SID, THIS FAT POOF'S GOT THE SAME HAIRCUT AS YE!

HOMOSEXUAL VICE RING EXPOSED

GUMPH!

47

The HIPPOPOTAMUS Man

One day reformed sex offender Derek Bagshaw awoke. To discover that he had suddenly developed the ability to assume, more or less at will, certain limited characteristics of a hippopotamus.

MRS BAGSHAW? I'VE COME TO SEE YOUR SON DEREK. I'M HIS PAROLE OFFICER

AH YES. DO COME IN

DEREK. THERE'S A GENTLEMAN HERE TO SEE YOU

HELLO DEREK. HOW ARE YOU TODAY?

I'M AFRAID HE SPENDS ALL HIS TIME BURIED IN BOOKS ABOUT HIPPOPOTAMUSES. BUT AT LEAST HE'S NOT HANGING ABOUT OUTSIDE PUBLIC LAVATORIES ANYMORE, ARE YOU DEREK DEAR?

NO MUM

THAT'S GOOD. I'M VERY PLEASED WITH HIS PROGRESS

LATER... DEREK. I'M ABOUT TO MAKE YOUR TEA. COULD YOU BE A DEAR AND NIP TO THE BUTCHERS FOR HALF A POUND OF SAUSAGES

SOUNDS LIKE A JOB FOR...

....HIPPOPOTAMUS MAN!!

CHARACTERISTICS OF A HIPPOPOTAMUS!!

?

HIPPO-POTA-POW!

OH NO. NOT AGAIN!

GRUNT GRUNT! GRUNT GRUNT!

I WISH YOU WOULDN'T DO THAT, DEREK. YOU'VE WET YOURSELF AGAIN

NO MOTHER. I HAVEN'T. I'M WALLOWING IN WATER. TO ESCAPE THE HEAT OF THE MIDDAY SUN

JUST ONE OF MANY HIPPOPOTAMUS CHARACTERISTICS WHICH I NOW POSESS

HIPPOPOTAMUS CHARACTERISTICS WHICH YOU NOW POSESS INDEED! GET YOURSELF OFF TO THE BUTCHERS THIS INSTANT

COUPLE OF PROBLEMS THERE MUM

FIRSTLY, I AM **RESTFUL** DURING THE DAY, FORAGING FOR FOOD **AT NIGHT**. AN AFTERNOON VISIT TO THE BUTCHERS – HALF A MILE AWAY– WOULD THEREFORE BE ENTIRELY OUT OF CHARACTER. SECONDLY, HIPPOPOTAMUSES ARE **VEGETARIAN**...

... SO I DON'T WANT SAUSAGES FOR TEA

DON'T WANT SAUSAGES FOR TEA INDEED! WELL YOU CAN JOLLY WELL GET OUT AND FORAGE FOR YOUR OWN TEA!

GRUNT! SQUEAL!!

BOOT!

WHILST MY DISPOSITION MAY GENERALLY BE DESCRIBED AS PLACID, THERE ARE NUMEROUS RECORDED INSTANCES OF APARENTLY UNPROVOKED ATTACKS ON HUMANS BY HIPPOPOTAMUSES. MOTHER WOULD DO WELL TO REMEMBER THAT!

TO THE PARK

LATER, IN THE PARK...

TWEET! TWEET! TWEET!

GRUNT!

GRUNT!

THE PARK

HEY MISTER. PLEASE SAVE MY BOAT. IT'S FLOATING AWAY!

I'M SORRY SON. I'M HIPPOPOTAMUS MAN. I'M **PONDEROUS** AND **BULKY**. I COULD **NEVER** REACH YOUR BOAT

BUT SURELY THE HIPPOPOTAMUS, DESPITE ITS WEIGHT (A LARGE MALE WEIGHING UP TO 4 TONS) IS AN **EXCELLENT SWIMMER!**

UNFORTUNATELY THAT IS ONE CHARACTERISTIC OF THE HIPPOPOTAMUS THAT I HAVE NOT ACQUIRED

HOY YOU! STOP FORAGING IN THOSE DAFFODILS OR I'LL CALL THE POLICE!!

PARKIE

BLOODY PARKIE! WHAT'S HIS PROBLEM?

I'VE SEEN MY NATURAL HABITAT DRAMATICALLY ERODED BY MAN OVER THE LAST CENTURY. ALL HE CARES ABOUT IS HIS FUCKING DAFFODILS!

AH! THANK GOODNESS YOU'VE ARRIVED OFFICER. A STOUT MAN, EXHIBITING CERTAIN LIMITED CHARACTERISTICS OF A HIPPOPOTAMUS, HAS BEEN WADING IN THE LAKE AND FORAGING IN MY DAFFODILS.

OH HE HAS, HAS HE?

YES. HE WAS LAST SEEN HEADING IN THE DIRECTION OF THE PUBLIC LAVATORIES.

AND...

TELL ME BOYS. HAVE YOU EVER SEEN A HIPPOPOTAMUSES' WILLIE?

TOILETS

I'M SCARED. I WANT TO GO HOME

48

JURASSIC GARDENS

Greenfingered stars could play host to dinosaurs

In the millions of years since dinosaurs last roamed the Earth many changes have taken place in our environment. Continents have been torn apart, mountains thrown up out of the sea and huge oceans created by melting ice.

So what would dinosaurs make of our planet today? How would these giant reptiles react to our motorways, our high rise blocks and our huge, sprawling cities. And how, for example, would these pre-historic monsters adapt to living in the gardens of some of TV's best known stars?

DETAILS

We fed details of some of the best kept gardens of the stars into a special dinosaur computer. And we were surprised by some of the results. For they suggested that the gardens of many of Britain's top celebrities and entertainers could prove to be ideal homes for large dinosaurs.

PATROLS

As well as being a respected broadcaster and celebrated sexual deviant, TV's **FRANK BOUGH** is also a renowned authority on dinosaurs. He has written many books on the subject including *'Let's Be Frank – Frank Bough's Earnest Opinion of Dinosaurs',* and *'Dinosaurs – A Grandstand View by Frank Bough.'* So we asked Frank to sift through our dinosaur data and pinpoint exactly which celebrities' gardens would be best suited to accommodating these gigantic extinct reptiles of the Jurassic era.

MICRAS

"Dinosaurs like a wet environment", said Frank. "Huge and slow moving, they would spend a lot of their time partly submerged in water. For that reason we are looking for a garden with either a pond or a swimming pool, or perhaps both.

They also eat trees, and so plenty of high vegetation is another must. A nice row of coniferous hedges –Llaylandi for example – would be ideal, as these are fast growing and could be replanted after they'd been eaten up by dinosaurs.

PRIMERAS

A further consideration would be wildlife. Some dinosaurs, such as the Tyranosaurus, were meat eaters, and they would need a supply of food in order to survive. A household with

pets – cats and dogs for example – would be an advantage. Or ideally a garden with a rabbit problem. Rabbits can do untold harm to plants in your garden, but a hungry dinosaur would soon put a stop to that, I can tell you".

SUNNIES

Frank also warned of some of the dangers to dinosaurs that are inherent in many of the gardens of the stars. "I'd be very weary of overhead wires such as telephone cables and electricity supplies. Dinosaurs are very tall, and don't exactly have brilliant eyesight, so they'd be prone to all sorts of accidents.

Also a busy driveway, with cars coming and going, could be a danger to both drivers and dinosaurs. Dinosaurs might be scared of cars, but then again they might mistake them for other dinosaurs, and try to have a fight with them", said Frank.

RAINIES

Finally we gave Frank sketch plans of the gardens of several top stars from the world of TV entertainment, and asked him to pick a top three, judging each garden on its own individual suitability for dinosaurs.

"I must say it was a difficult choice, but in third place I've chosen the garden of keen golfer **BRUCE FORSYTH.** Bruce's garden is spacious, with room for quite a few dinosaurs. He has a pond, lots of trees, and plenty of grass for them to walk around on.

WINDIES

"The only minus factor in Brucie's garden is the fact that the dinosaurs would probably make big footholes in the putting green which Bruce uses for putting practice. But apart from that, an excellent garden for dinosaurs".

DOORS

In second place Frank plumped for the unusually small garden of former Neighbours heart throb **JASON DONOVAN.**
"I chose Jason's small back garden behind his London flat because of the many trees which overhang it from the adjoining park.

BRUCIE: Room for lots of dinosaurs

Busy Jason has no time for uphill gardening

Chris's garden is ideal for a dip.

Although it would only be big enough for one small dinosaur, providing it's neck was long enough it would certainly have plenty to eat. And because Jason spends very little time in his garden, due to his hectic showbusiness commitments, he probably wouldn't mind a dinosaur in it".

WAALS

In first place Frank chose a worthy winner – the garden of TV funster **CHRIS TARRANT.**

GARDEN

"Chris has a nice big garden, but its main advantages is that it borders onto

a river. Dinosaurs could roam happily in Chris's orchard, sit around on the patio if they wanted, and then take a dip in the river to take some of the weight off their legs. I'd say that without a doubt Chris's garden would be my number one choice for accommodating dinosaurs".

ARE YOU CLIFF RICHARD'S LOVECHILD?

Without scientific evidence it is often impossible to prove whether or not you are Cliff Richard's lovechild. So here's a special questionnaire that we've designed to enable you to do your very own home test – and discover once and for all whether your mum dropped a Cliff clanger.

But the Peter Pan of Pop has nothing to fear. Because we've declared a special amnesty on all Cliff's love children. And if your answers reveal that you are the son or daughter of Cliff, we'll pay your maintenance in order to protect Britain's best loved pop singer from the harmful publicity this could generate.

FANS

Let's face it. Most of our mothers were fans of Cliff Richard. And even Cliff himself admits to sleeping with at least **one** women. So let's put your mind at rest once and for all with this easy to answer questionnaire.

CHANCE

Anyone can answer, but in order to avoid disappointment we must point out that to stand a reasonable chance of being Cliff's lovechild you must be **younger** than Cliff himself.

1. Which of the following would be your ideal holiday?
(a) A raunchy fortnight with your mates on the Costa del Sol.
(b) A week spent in a quiet cottage in remote Wales or Cornwall.
(c) Touring in the South of France in a big red bus with Una Stubbs and Melvyn Hayes.

2. You're about to catch a train. You nip into WH Smith to buy a book to read during your journey. What sort of book would you choose?
(a) A raunchy paperback, with a partially naked woman on the cover.
(b) An informative book, about gardening, cookery or a subject that interests you.
(c) The Bible.

3. Imagine that you have discovered the Christian faith. You begin to question the commercial exploitation of Christmas, which is, after all, a religious festival celebrating the birth of Christ. What would you do?
(a) Boycott Christmas altogether, refusing to celebrate it in any way.
(b) Shun all commercial aspects of Christmas, and try to get back to the religious basis.
(c) Bring out a crappy Christmas single with sleigh-bells and a choir singing and a book called 'Christmas with Cliff' featuring yourself on the cover, dressed as Santa Claus.

4. How difficult would you say it is for a rich man to enter into the gates of heaven?
(a) Pretty hard.
(b) Harder than for a camel to pass through the eye of a needle.
(c) Not very hard at all, really.

5. If you were a celebrity, what would be your idea of a sporting day out?
(a) A day at the races with Alex Higgins, sticking a few quid on the gee-gees.
(b) A round of golf with Tarby and Bruce Forsyth, and a few drinks afterwards at the nineteenth.
(c) A game of tennis with Sue Barker.

6. What sort of drugs do you take?
(a) Dope, coke, heroin.. whatever you can get, whenever you can get it.
(b) Parecetamol for your head. Kaolin for your arse. That's about it.
(c) None. Drugs are not for you.

7. What did you think of The Beatles?
(a) Great. They were the best band ever.
(b) Good, but they've been a little over rated in the past.
(c) I thought they were okay until they started taking drugs, getting into weird religions and sleeping with girls.

8. Go and look in the mirror. How would you describe your neck?
(a) Smooth, young looking with soft skin.
(b) A bit aged, with wrinkles, but not exceptional.
(c) Leathery, like a dinosaur's scrotum.

9. If totally unfounded rumours began circulating that you wore a colostomy bag (some ludicrous variations of which involved an alleged incident at Mile End tube station in the sixties), how would you react?
(a) Deny them at every available opportunity, and threaten to sue the perpetrators.
(b) Flatly deny them, and threaten to sue the perpetrators.
(c) Maintain your dignity by refusing to stoop so low as to even acknowledge that such malicious and patently untruthful rumours exist.

10. How do you see yourself in later life?
(a) Married, with kids, a car and a house.
(b) Living with a regular partner, but avoiding the commitments of marriage.
(c) You'll be a batchelor boy, and that's the way you'll stay-ay-ay-ay. Yes, you'll be a batchelor boy, until your dying day.

How did you do?

Now tot up your score. Award yourself 1 point for each answer (a), two points for (b), and three points for (c). If your score comes to 27 or more, there exists a strong likelihood that you are Cliff Richard's lovechild, and you may qualify for maintenance payments under our 'Coughing up for Cliff's Clangers' scheme.

The next step is to send us a photograph of yourself, together with a photo of Cliff Richard looking similar. Our judges' decision will be final in all cases. If our judges find in your favour, maintenance payments will be made to you discreetly by post.

Fill in the following form and enclose it with your photograph. Please remember to mark your envelope 'I suspect I may be Cliff's love child'. This competition is not open to former Shadow Jet Harris, his family, friends or relatives. No correspondence will be entered into. The judges decision will be final.

To: Cliff's Clangers, Viz, P.O. Box 1PT, Newcastle upon Tyne NE99 1PT.

I scored _____ in the Cliff questionnaire and therefore have reasonable grounds to suspect that Cliff Richard is my true father. I enclose a photo of me and one of Cliff looking slightly similar. If maintenance payments are made to me I promise not to go to the News of the World.

Signed _____

Address for maintenance payments _____

_____

HAVE YOU DONE ANY WORK PAID OR UNPAID SINCE YOU LAST SIGNED ON?

NO...

SIR... I... HAVE... NOT!

NEVER! NEVER! NEVER!

SIGN HERE PLEASE.

ERM... BRAVO. BRAVO. LUVVIE YOU WERE SO WONDERFUL. EVERYONE'S TALKING ABOUT YOU. THEY'RE CALLING YOU THE NEW OLIVIER.

AH! THE RRROAR OF THE CROWD, THE SMELL OF THE GREASEPAINT! IT'S ALL SIMPLY SO ADORABLE!!!

COME ON DEAR. LET'S GO HOME NOW!

SORRY DEAR. I'M MEETING MY AGENT AT ELEVEN.

WE'RE TAKING DRINKIE-WINKIES AT THE GARRICKY-WARRICKY.

SHORTLY...

HELLO! MMMWAH! MMMWAH!

LUVVIE MY BOY!

MMWAH! MMWAH!

DID YOU CATCH MY APPEARANCE AT THE D.H.S.S?

NO. BUT I HEARD YOU WERE A TRIUMPH LUVVIE - A TRIUMPH!!

YOU'RE THE TOAST OF THE LABOUR EXCHANGE!

YES. I WAS RAATHER MARVELLOUS SEVERAL CRITICS IN THE CIRCLE WERE MOVED TO TEARS DON'T YOU KNOW. I REMINDED MYSELF OF NOTHING SO MUCH AS DEAR SIR RALPHIE'S SCOTTISH PLAY AT THE COTTESLOE IN '62.

ANYWAY LUVVIE - YOU REMEMBER THAT AUDITION YOU DID LAST WEEK? - WELL YOU GOT THE PART! IT'S THE BIG ONE, LUVVIE - IT'S HAMLET. THEY START FILMING TOMORROW.

ABSOLUTELY WA-NDERFUL! AT LAST- MY DEFINITIVE PERFORMANCE CAPTURED FOR POSTERITY.

YES. OH, AND BY THE WAY, MY FEE'S GONE UP TO 90%.

NEXT MORNING...

PINE LODGE STUDIOS

5mph

MAKE-UP, COSTUME & HUGGING STRAIGHT ON

AND...

LIGHTS! CAMERA! ACTION!

SOUND STAGE 1B

SMOKEY JOE'S FAG SHOP ADVERT - TAKE ONE!

DIRECTOR

AND... CUE LUVVIE!!

20 King Size

CIGARS ARE HALF PRICE AT SMOKEY JOE'S FAG SHOP THIS THURSDAY!

CUT!

PILOT MATCHES

TUESDAY! TUESDAY! TUESDAY!

STUDIO 1B

CIGARS ARE HALF PRICE... CIGARS ARE... CIGARS ARE HALF PRICE AT SMOKEY JOE'S THIS TUESDAY... THIS TUESDAY.

EXIT

OH COME ON LUVVIE. YOU'RE A PROFESSIONAL. MAKE IT MORE "CIGAR"!

LETTER BOCKS

Mix-up over bill

LetterBocks
Viz Commick
P.O. Box 1 PT
Newcasle upon Tyne
NE99 1PT

While dining out in a restaurant with a group of friends we were amused when the waitress offered to get the bill. "We are the bill", we told her. She had to laugh when she realised we were in fact the cast and crew of the popular three times weekly ITV police drama 'The Bill'.

The cast and crew of the popular three times weekly ITV police drama The Bill, London.

If Linda McCartney would stop trying to sing, do hand claps and play mini-moog on Paul's records, I will become a vegetarian and so will three of my mates.

So come on Linda. Which is more important – pretending to be a pop star, or the lives of countless innocent farm animals?

P. Abbott
Newent

Film actor forgets film

I am the British film actor Sir John Mills, and I was wondering whether any of your readers could help me recall the name of that film I was in where we all lived in house, and I went to sea during the war. As best I recall it started with us moving into the house. It was that long ago the name completely escapes me.

Sir John Mills
British Film Actor

Looking through the Highway Code the other day I was unable to find the rule which tells London bus drivers to pull out into the road whilst still occupied with taking money from passengers, having indicated their intention to do so for at least three minutes beforehand. Perhaps my edition is a misprint.

P. J. Taylor
Amersham

Following on from Mr Abbott's letter (Viz, this issue). How would Linda McCartney feel if Paul kept lending a hand with her vegetarian recipes, started putting sausages in everything and burning her veggie burgers?

J. Strap
Leeds

How about a picture of my favourite sea bird – the puffin?

P. Oxley
London N5

Come on readers. Who's got a picture of a puffin? Send them to our special Letterbocks Puffin Picture Request Desk at the usual address. There's a crisp tenner for the sender of every picture we use.

I've got horn for blow job

I just had to tell your readers about the most sensational blow job I got the other day off a middle aged bird who was wearing a pin striped skirt and jacket. She runs an entertainments agency, and got me a 6 month contract playing trumpet on board the QE2.

B. Balderstone
Peterlee

I used to look forward to Sunday, the one night of the week when I would stay in to wash my hair. But since changing brands to 'Wash and Go' I now feel obliged to go out afterwards. I think the shampoo manufacturers are putting unnecessary pressure on women.

Miss S. Head
Lambeth, London SW8

Bird's arse pic request

It's been almost 5 issues since you last printed that picture of a bloke kissing that bird's arse. Have you lost it? If so, how about a repeat of that picture of Catherine Zeta-Jones in her underwear?

Mr F. Ish
Glenfield, Leicester

Come on, readers. Let's have a vote on it. Which picture would you rather see? A bloke kissing that bird's arse, or Catherine Zeta-Jones in a bra. Postcards please to the usual address. The winning picture will appear on our next letters page.

Any old port

I'm presently stuck on a UN peace keeping tour of the old Yugoslavia. Is there any chance of a picture of Grimsby, as I miss the place terribly. If not, any similar North sea fishing port would do. Except Hull.

C. W. Sparkes
Vitez

I noticed with some interest that Dirty Den, alias real-life TV actor Leslie Grantham, is appearing in the new series of the ITV murder mystery game show 'Cluedo'. Surely the solution each week will be the same. 'It was Leslie Grantham, in the back of a taxi, with a revolver'.

C. Mustard
Catterick

"Life is a cabaret", or so the song goes. Well, I can assure Miss Lisa Minelli that I for one do **not** spend my time dressed in fishnet tights and a top hat straddling the backs of dining chairs like a tuppenny whore.

Mr K. Tell
Bromsgrove

They say 'all men are potential rapists'. Well I'm not. I'm a convicted one.

G. Barchester
H.M. Prison Hull

To say that the whole country has gone to the dogs is something of an exaggeration. At my local greyhound stadium last night I counted less than 300 people.

Matthew Cope
Swindon

Blowing my own trumpet

Without wanting to sound boastful, I woke up this morning with the most magnificent erection, even if I do say so myself.

Flav
Birmingham

I'm sick up to the back teeth with old folk who retire to newly built bungalows because they can't be bothered to go up stairs any more. They don't mind a hike to the Post Office every couple of weeks to collect their pensions, do they?

D. Grace
Nantwich

Why do so many people waste money every year on Comic Relief red plastic noses and tomatoes for the front of their cars? Surely it would serve a greater purpose if they donated the money to charity instead of frittering it on these cheap, plastic comedy gimmicks.

Martine
Oxford

TOP-TIPS

LOOK like a hunky body builder by buying a vest or T-shirt that's too small for you and walking around like you've got a roll of carpet under each arm.

Hapag Lloyd again
Runcorn

SAVE money on expensive nicotine gum by chewing ordinary gum and smoking a cigarette at the same time.

H. Cavender
Kingston

FEMINISTS. Convince men you're all killjoys by combing adult comics in search of something to whine about then making cliched jibes in the letters page about penile size. Better yet, don't use your own name but write on behalf of some pompous self-regarding wimmin's group.

Douglas Porter
Norfolk

GET RID of irritating pieces of meat stuck between your teeth by popping a handful of maggots into your mouth and allowing them to crawl around your gums for a few minutes after each meal.

I. Meatgon
Nottingham

GIRLS. When applying cosmetics in a mirror place a second mirror on a table or chair behind you. Look over your shoulder in the first mirror to see yourself reflected in the second mirror to see what your make-up will actually look like to others, rather than the usual reversed image reflection obtained in a single mirror.

J. Sulzer
Ipswich

GET the feel of camping outdoors without the inconveniences of the real thing by turning off the heating, releasing ants on your bedroom carpet, crapping on the floor, then sleeping on it, wrapped in a plastic bin liner.

Graeme Marsh
Ashford

HOUSEWIVES. Throw a fish carcass into a bucket of cement and, hey presto! When it dries you have an instant fossil.

Tam Dale
High Blantyre, Glasgow

OBTAIN the effect of satellite TV by painting a dustbin lid white and nailing it onto an outside wall, then filling a fish tank with shit and sitting staring at it for 23 hours a day.

J. Brush
Loughborough

DROP a table tennis ball into public urinals and invite other toilet users to play 'piss tennis' by directing the ball backwards and forwards along the bottom of the urinal with your wees.

J. Naylor
Northwich

DISAPPOINT wasps this summer by smearing cold tea on your ears instead of honey.

T. Shankborne
Coventry

GIRLS! This summer make sure you don't miss out on a tan. Go topless at the slightest hint of sunshine.

Rob Walker
Harrow, London

ENCOURAGE friends to telephone you by offering a plastic dinosaur for every call.

H. Lloyd
Runcorn. Again

DON'T throw away those old car batteries. Placed inside an old pillow case, they make an ideal counter balance on a see-saw.

Alex
Burnley

DRIVERS. When on the continent simplify driving on the 'wrong' side of the road by placing your rear view mirror above your back windscreen. Then simply look over your shoulder whilst driving and view the road ahead in the re-positioned mirror. Everything will appear perfectly normal, with cars driving on the 'left' side of the road

J. Sulzer
Ipswich

CAN'T find a dictionary? Try a telephone directory. They contain many useful words, such as cooper, black and smart, all of which are listed in alphabetical order.

R. Clayton
Arbroath

Secret side of the stars

Let's face it! We all recognise our favourite TV faces. We can all picture our favourite TV star, seen from the front.
But how different do they look viewed from an angle? Would you recognise that famous face if you saw it from the side?

BLUE

In fact it wasn't until 1972 that British TV viewers saw their first sideways view of a celebrity, when 'Generation Game' host Bruce Forsyth made history by inviting Anthea Redfern to "give us a twirl". The leggy lovely spun her way into broadcasting history by revolving in a complete circle before the cameras.

MANALITO

Another TV beauty instantly recognised by men is delicious Darling Bud Catherine Zeta Jones. From the front we are struck by her stunning brown hair, her alluring eyes and her lovely lips. But, as anyone lucky enough to have had a sideways view of the budding star will tell you, her face is remarkably flat, a bit like a dustbin lid.

VICTORIA

"She's not unattractive to look at - quite the opposite - but you don't realise how flat her face is until you see her from the side", one TV insider told us. Indeed some sources are claimed to have compared Catherine's round, flat face to Weed out of Bill and Ben.

WATERLOO

Female viewers would no doubt drool over any TV appearances by DJ Gary Davis. He was, until fairly recently, one of Radio One's top pop presenters. And when he hosted Top Of The Pops TV viewers saw what appeared to be a not unattractive young man with nice teeth.

MAMA MIA

But for the handful of viewers watching from the studio audience, their sideways view of Gary told a different story. For the likeable DJ has been cursed with a rather prominent posterior. Indeed, it was once said that you could stand a vase of flowers on it. Although there may have been an element of exaggeration involved in that particular claim, witnesses would not deny that from the side, Gary's bottom does stick out. A bit.

FERNANDO

American TV actor James Garner is another star with a peculiar profile. Best known for his role as TV's Jim Rockford, a rare sideways glance at the tough private detective would reveal that the back of his head doesn't actually exist. "Rather than having a top on his head, then a vertical drop down to his neck, he

Sideways glance reveals peculiar profiles

just has a slope from the top of his eyebrows down to his shirt collar", one seventies TV viewer vaguely recalled yesterday.

TIMES

Of course it is the TV news readers whose heads we most often view from the front. And often it is they who have the most peculiar profiles. For example, 'Newsnight' veteran Peter Snow is known as 'Mr Punch' among his BBC2 colleagues , because of his unusual 'hooky' nose and chin.

A darling bud and a cardboard flower. Catherine (above) and her Bill & Ben TV look-a-like.

MIRROR

Nowadays modern technology and newscasting techniques have lead to more revealing angles being adopted by news readers. Twin news readers on ITN's 'News At Ten' are occasionally called upon to look at one another, giving viewers a fascinating flash of a three-quarter profile. And Jeremy Paxman regularly turns his neck through 90 degrees to aim a stern question directly at a guest, giving his many fans a perfect lateral elevation of his tall, rather narrow head.

BIFF! SMACK! POW!

Is this the end for Captain Jazzmag?

There's bad news for fans of our horny superhero *Captain Jazzmag*. In the last issue he offered to come to the rescue of randy readers and send them the dirty magazine of their choice for a modest £10 fee.

Unfortunately Jazzmag has been **ZAPPED!** by an arch rival superhero. But not before ten seedy readers sent £10 each in return for porny mags. Enter *Captain Blackmail*.

Our new superhero Captain Blackmail is now in possession of all ten names and addresses of readers who placed orders and were supplied with filthy mags. And he was **DISGUSTED** when he realised the nature of the publications Captain Jazzmag was supplying.

BRIEFLY

Briefly, flicking through some of the ten titles before they were posted off, Captain Blackmail was SICKENED to find lurid photographs of naked and semi-naked young women. One smiled provocatively as she raised her bottom in the air. Another licked her lips while her hand rested suggestively on her naked bosom. The Captain was:

● **SHOCKED** by scenes of a naked woman immersed in a frothy bubble bath.

● **STUNNED** by the image of a buxom blonde who clasped her heaving breasts firmly in her hands, and

● **ENORMOUSLY AROUSED** by one hamburger shot in particular.

VESTLY

The sick individuals who ordered this **FILTH** to be delivered to their homes have every reason to be concerned. For Captain Blackmail is an enemy of pornography, and he issued them with the following warning.

Horny hero ZAPPED by righteous rival

"Unless the ten readers who ordered the dirty books send me another £10 each, then I will have no choice but to print their full names and addresses in the next issue. They know who they are, and unless they cough up the cash, so will millions of other readers including their friends and their families".

SOCKLY

The guilty parties should send their extra cash to Captain Blackmail together with the form below. If your money is not received by the last day of June, then J.W. of Crewe, B.B. of Glasgow, M.L. of Leicester, Mr W. of Cardiff, P.G. of West Ham, A.T. of Reading, Mr J. of Ilkley, S.F. of Warrington, H.C. of Manchester and A.K. of

Middlesbrough will be fully introduced to our estimated 8 million readers in the next issue.

Footnote: In the last issue Captain Jazzmag may have mistakenly given readers the impression that he was offering copies of Penthouse magazine for sale. It has been brought to our attention by the publishers of Penthouse that their magazine is not a porny mag at all, more of a sophisticated gentleman's title. The Captain offers his assurance that no copies of Penthouse were supplied to readers, and indeed none were ordered.

Razzle, on the other hand, was well popular with our ten perverts, proving itself to be far and away Britain's top scud mag.

To: Captain Blackmail, Viz, P.O. Box 1PT, Newcastle upon Tyne, NE99 1PT.

Dear Captain Blackmail,

I sincerely regret my foolhardy decision to buy a pornographic magazine from your predecessor Captain Jazzmag. I enclose £10 to stop you publishing my name and address in the next issue.

Signed _____

Address _____

NO SEGS PLEASE WE'RE BRITISH

British shoe wearers are saying 'no' to segs. And that's official.

According to a survey published this week the 'Golden Era' of British seg wearing was the fifties, with 8 out of 10 men inserting the metal sole protectors in the bottoms of their shoes. But nowadays, the survey reveals, as little as 1 in 50 adults own shoes that are fitted with segs.

SEGS

The independent report into seg wearing was commissioned by the Association of British Seg Manufacturers and Retailers, and was produced by a committee headed by former police chief John Stalker. In his conclusion Mr Stalker points out that segs cannot be worn in many of today's most popular types of shoe, especially training shoes, as these do not have leather soles.

Brits boycott Blakeys

However, according to EEC figures, seg wearing in other European nations is on the increase. And top of the table of Euro seg wearers are the Norweigans, with seg sales up by an increadible 1000 per cent over the last two years. In 1992 segs mad Scandinavians bought a phenomenal 18 million segs, compared to only 72 segs sold in Britain in the same period.

BEGGS

But the signs are that British seg sales could be picking up. One cobbler we spoke to today told us that he had sold two Blakeys half moon segs yesterday. And a tin of *Kiwi* boot polish.

Morris 'n' Monkeys

No. 63 DESMOND MORRIS

MOUSE MAN DIES

A man who caught a mouse in the kitchen of TV tough guy cop Taggart has been killed in gardening accident – days before his book detailing the incident was due to be published.

Pest control operative Frank Hamilton had planned to use the proceeds from his book to take his wife and family to Australia where he had hoped to set up his own business catching rabbits and then drowning them in a bucket.

HOE

Mr Hamilton, who was 56, died when a hoe he was wielding hit overhead power cables at the garden of his home in Polmadie. Neighbours described a loud bang followed by a buzzing noise.

Extracts from Mr Hamilton's book were due to be published in this magazine and are refered to on the cover. However, in the light

of Mr Hamilton's tragic death publication of the book has been postponed.

THERE'S A MOOSE LOOSE ABOOT THIS HOOSE

The page that never was. This is how the extracts from Mr Hamilton's book were set to look before his tragic death.

Billy the Fish

IN THE LAST EPISODE FULCHESTER BOSS TOMMY BROWN SHAT ON HIS DESK. IN THE RESULTING FURORE WE CHALLENGED DISGUSTED READERS TO SEND IN 20p IF THEY WANTED BILLY THE FISH AXED. A TOTAL OF £10 WAS ALL WE REQUIRED TO PUT THE LONG-SUFFERING READERS OF THE COMIC'S LEAST POPULAR STRIP OUT OF THEIR MISERY. BUT ALAS ONLY £5.60 WAS RAISED - AND SO THE AGONY MUST CONTINUE AS WE COMMENCE THE 51st EPISODE OF BILLY THE FISH.

BUT JUST BEFORE WE GET UNDERWAY, TOP SOLICITOR RICHARD HART-TRANSPLANT WILL READ A STATEMENT ON BEHALF OF FULCHESTER BOSS TOMMY BROWN.

MY CLIENT WISHES TO APOLOGISE TO ALL READERS FOR THE REGRETTABLE INCIDENT DURING THE LAST EPISODE WHEN HE WAS CLEARLY SEEN TO PASS A RECTAL STOOL UPON HIS DESK TOP.

PRIOR TO THIS UNFORTUNATE EVENT MR BROWN HAD BEEN SUFFERING FROM NERVOUS EXHAUSTION DUE TO THE RIGOURS AND STRESSES OF APPEARING IN THIS LONG-RUNNING AND WIDELY DISLIKED STRIP CARTOON.

THAT'LL BE 200 GUINEAS PLEASE MR. BROWN.

WOOF! WOOF!

QUACK! QUACK! GIBBER GIBBER!

THE FOLLOWING MORNING THE PLAYERS ARRIVE AT FULCHESTER STADIUM FOR TRAINING...

THAT'S ODD BILLY. TOMMY BROWN'S LATE.

FUNNY. IT'S NOT LIKE HIM TO MISS A TRAINING SESSION.

DON'T WORRY. I'LL GO OUT AND LOOK FOR HIM. I'M SURE THERE'S A PERFECTLY SIMPLE EXPLANATION.

SYD HEADED STRAIGHT FOR TOMMY'S BIG HOUSE IN THE COUNTRY.

I THINK I'LL TAKE AN UNLIKELY SHORT-CUT THROUGH THIS FIELD.

HELLO - WHAT'S THIS? A PILE OF PISS-STAINED RAGS LYING IN MY PATH?

WAIT A MINUTE. IT'S NOT A URINE-DRENCHED HEAP OF RUBBISH AFTER ALL! IT'S...

GROAN...

PROD

IT'S... TOMMY BROWN!

DRINK PROBLEM? ME? HIC!? RUBBISH.

YOU'RE NOT WELL, BRI...ER... TOMMY. YOU NEED A REST.

I'LL SHOOT ANYONE WHO SAYS I'VE GOT A DRINK PROBLEM, YOUNG MAN.

MY GRANDCHILDREN LAUGH AT ME FOR NOT HAVING ANY 'O' LEVELS.

DO YOU KNOW WHAT I TELL THEM?

I SAY LOOK AT THESE. THESE ARE MY 'O' LEVELS. BIG, BROWN, STEAMING 'O' LEVELS! CAN YOU SEE THEM SYD? CAN YOU SEE MY 'O' LEVELS?

COME ON TOMMY. THAT'S ENOUGH. YOU NEED HELP. COME WITH ME.

AND ANYWAY, WHAT'S WRONG WITH SLEEPING IN A FIELD? I ALWAYS SLEEP IN FIELDS.

...AND I'LL SHOOT ANYONE WHO SAYS OTHERWISE.

DRINK PROBLEM? WHAT DRINK PROBLEM? I JUST HAVE A FEW BOTTLES OF COOKING SHERRY AT WORK AND TEN CANS OF LAGER ON THE WAY HOME...

BACK AT FULCHESTER STADIUM, A BITTER BOARDROOM POWER STRUGGLE IS REACHING ITS CLIMAX AS REBEL SHAREHOLDER SIR WINYARD HALL RISES TO HIS FEET...

I, AS LEADER OF THE BREAKAWAY CUCKOO GROUP, PROPOSE A VOTE OF NO CONFIDENCE IN THE CHAIRMAN OF THIS FOOTBALL CLUB.

BUT SINCE THE EMERGENCY BOARD MEETING LAST NIGHT YOU ARE THE CHAIRMAN SIR JOH... ER, SIR WINYARD.

OH I SEE.

RIGHT. IN THAT CASE, I HEREBY SACK THE MANAGER - MR. TOMMY BROWN - AND WISH TO ANNOUNCE THE APPOINTMENT OF HIS SUCCESOR...

MR. KELVIN KOOGAN - THE FORMER KIDNEYPOOL, SV HAMBURGER, MOUTHAMPTON AND ENGLAND CAPTAIN.

THE NEXT DAY IN MANAGER KELVIN KOOGAN'S OFFICE...

AH SYD. YOU WANTED TO SEE ME.

YES MR. KOOGAN.

SIT DOWN SYD.

WHAT'S ON YOUR MIND?

WELL FRANKLY I'D LIKE TO KNOW WHERE I STAND NOW THAT TOMMY'S LEFT. DO I STILL HAVE A FUTURE HERE AT FULCHESTER?

YES SYD.

YOUR JOB IS SAFE.

BUT FROM NOW ON, I'D LIKE YOU TO WEAR THIS CURLY PERM WIG AND FALSE 'BROOKSIDE' TASH.

...AND TALK IN A SCOUSE ACCENT.

TANKS BOSS. DAT'S TRIFFIKKH. SOUND. BUT WE'D BERRA HURRY UP AND GET TO DER DUG-OUT, DOH DERE'S A MATCH KICKKHIN' OFF IN 2 MINUTES.

SHORTLY, IN THE DUG-OUT...
WHO ARE WE PLAYING TODAY TERRY?...ERM...I MEAN SYD.
SOVEREIGNTY CITY BOSS. IT'S A GRUDGE MATCH LIKKH.

THEY'RE FIELDING EX-FULCHESTER STAR THE MIGHTY QUINN - THE 70'S AMERICAN WRESTLER WHOM FEW READERS WILL HAVE HEARD OF.

NOT TO WORRY. MY NEW SIGNING WILL BE MORE THAN A MATCH FOR THAT FAT YANKEE FALL-GUY.
YES. SO WHO IS THIS AT No 10? ALL IT SAYS ON THE TEAMSHEET IS SHIRLEY CRABTREE.
THAT'S RIGHT SYD. SHIRLEY CRABTREE - OTHERWISE KNOWN AS...

...BIG DADDY!

SECONDS LATER, THE MATCH KICKS OFF, AND SOVEREIGNTY ARE QUICKLY ON THE ATTACK...
I'M BEATEN!

HANG ON THOUGH. BIG DADDY LOOKS SET TO CHALLENGE THE MIGHTY QUINN FOR THE BALL.
YES.

SPLASH!
GREAT BODY CHECK BY THE RED FACED 42-STONE PORKER WITH A GIRL'S NAME!

LAYDEEE2 ANNN GENNELMENNN! THEEE WINNERRR! BY THREE FALLS ANN ERRR SUBMISSIONNERRR! MY BROTHERRR! BEEEEG! DADDEEEEE!
EAS-EH! EAS-EH!

MEANWHILE, SHAKIN' STEVENS FEEDS BROWN FOX, ON THE EDGE OF THE SIX YARD BOX...

SHAKIN' STEVENS HAS SOME SOCKS, WHICH HE KEEPS IN A CARDBOARD BOX.

A BOX WITH LOCKS AND LOTS OF CLOCKS AND SOCKS AND BLOCKS AND FOXES' COCKS.

MEANWHILE, IN THE BLUE PETER STUDIO...
£10
AS YOU CAN SEE, WE'RE JUST OVER HALF WAY ON OUR STOP BILLY THE FISH APPEAL.

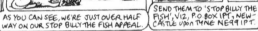

THE TOTALISER NOW STANDS AT £5.60. WE JUST NEED ANOTHER £4.40 TO REACH OUR TARGET.
YES. SO KEEP THOSE 20p'S COMING IN.
SEND THEM TO 'STOP BILLY THE FISH', VIZ, P.O. BOX 1PT, NEWCASTLE UPON TYNE NE99 1PT.

ON THURSDAY WE'LL SHOW YOU HOW TO MAKE A PAIR OF JOE 90 GLASSES USING 2 YOGHURT POTS AND SOME OLD CARPET.
GRAHAM DANGERFIELD WILL BE BRINGING AN ELEPHANT TO THE STUDIO TO CACK ON THE FLOOR...
AND I'LL TELL YOU WHAT IT'S LIKE TO GO TO BED WITH CATHERINE ZETA JONES OUT OF THE DARLING BUDS OF MAY. BECAUSE I HAVE.

BACK ON THE PITCH, FULCHESTER'S MICK HUCKNALL OUT OF SIMPLY RED FINDS HIMSELF UNMARKED IN THE 18 YARD BOX...
THIS IS MY BIG CHANCE!

...AND THE SOMETIME FATSO TURNS ON A SIXPENCE TO LASH HOME AN UNSTOPPABLE PILEDRIVER OF A SHOT!
GREAT GOAL!
YES!

WE'VE SCORED A GOAL SYD. THAT'S JUST THE START WE WERE LOOKING FOR.
YES BOSS - BUT I THINK WE MAY HAVE A PROBLEM.

UNFORTUNATELY, MICK INSISTS ON CELEBRATING HIS GOAL BY PERFORMING A HIGHLY DANGEROUS HUMAN CANNONBALL STUNT.
HMM. I CAN'T SAY I ALTOGETHER APPROVE OF SUCH FOOLHARDY BEHAVIOUR, SYD.

BANG!

WHEEE! I SCORED! LOOK AT ME! MICK HUCKNALL OUT OF SIMPLY RED!
HE'S GOING VERY HIGH!
UM YES.

OOPS!
BUT - THE SINGER'S HIGH JINKS CELEBRATIONS GO SERIOUSLY WRONG...

OH NO! HE'S LANDED IN THE GORILLA ENCLOSURE OF NEARBY FULCHESTER ZOO!

200 VISITORS LOOK ON HELPLESSLY AS THE MANCUNIAN SONGSTER LIES AT THE MERCY OF THE MAN-EATING GORILLAS...

WILL MICK HUCKNALL OUT OF SIMPLY RED BE DEVOURED BY MONKEYS IN FULCHESTER ZOO?

OR WILL READERS PUT AN END TO HIS - AND EVERYONE ELSE'S - SUFFERING, BY SENDING IN 20p?

REMEMBER - WE ONLY NEED ANOTHER £4.40 BEFORE OUR NEXT ISSUE GOES TO PRESS AND THERE WILL BE...

NO MORE BILLY THE FISH!

HOW WOULD THE STARS COOK THEMSELVES?

By our Cookery Writer

LIEUTENANT UHURA

Celebrities tend to travel by air more than most people. Their jet set lifestyles mean countless flights for the top names in the entertainment world.

But with air travel comes the unavoidable risk of tragedy. And it is therefore a grim fact of life that the stars could become the victims of an airline disaster. And this raises a number of questions that we, the paying public, have a right to ask.

CRASH

And top of the list must be: if, as a result of an aeroplane crash, some of our favourite stars were marooned on a remote mountain side, and cannibalism was their only hope of survival, how would they cook themselves?

BANG

First we asked EastEnders star **Anita Dobson** which of her cockney colleagues she would rather eat if the cast and crew of the popular soap found themselves stranded and starving on a windswept hillside in Peru.

Star eater Anita

"I'd have to go for Dirty Den, my on-screen husband and actor Leslie Grantham. Leslie and I enjoy working together and our on screen relationship is one of the strengths of the soap. But in the circumstances you describe I would reluctantly eat Leslie, but only if he was very well cooked, ideally on a barbecue."

POP

Stunning Darling Bud actress and pop starlette **Caterine Zeta-Jones** was given the choice of eating fellow members of the Darling Buds cast. And after a moments thought she said she'd prefer to eat Ma Larkin.

"I don't think anyone in my profession would relish the thought of eating a close friend and colleague, but I must admit the prospect of eating Ma – real life actress Pam Ferris – is far preferable to the idea of eating hairy old Pa or my on-screen husband whose name for the moment escapes me".

Star eater Catherine Zeta

Catherine wasn't so sure when it came to choosing a recipe for her screen mum. "I don't know... I suppose I'd like to roast her if that were possible in the circumstances. And I'd definitely want to wash her down with a bottle of wine to try and kill the taste".

WALLOP

We put a similar question to Catherine's former beau, hunky Blue Peter presenter **John Leslie**, himself a tasty dish. But on John's menu we listed a few appetising Blue Peter hosts of the past. And it was no surprise when John selected mouth watering Sarah Green as his choice for an emergency packed lunch.

"I must admit I'd be tempted by flâmbéted Valerie Singleton, and I'd quite fancy pickled John Noakes. But Sarah is the dish for me. And I'd have her in an omelette."

ROAST

When we asked Radio One FM's **Bruno Brookes** which of his DJ colleagues he'd prefer to eat we were surprised to find that he'd already given the subject some thought.

"Funnily enough, all the One FM jocks were flying back from a party in a plane

Celebrity cannibals serve up tasty star-packed dishes

Star eater John from Blue Peter

Simon B - the stars' tea

Sinead - Big Macca & fries

Star cook Bruno Brook...es

not so long ago when the weather turned nasty. The thought did cross all of our minds that we could go down, and that in order to survive one of us may have to be eaten. It was quite funny really. We all found ourselves looking at Simon Bates.

MASHED

In the end we landed safely, and Bates is still in one piece. But hypothetically speaking, if I did have to cook him I think it would have to be boiled, in a big pot, with lots of herbs thrown in".

CHIPS

Finally we popped the question to controversial pop star **Sinead O'Connor**. We asked her whether her strict vegetarian principles would allow her to eat a fellow star if it meant the differecne between life and death. Surprisingly she had no qualms about tucking into a music industry colleague.

"Yes, I would reluctantly eat a fellow artist in order to stay alive. But I would insist on eating a fellow vegetarian to ensure that there was no animal protien in their body. I would choose Linda McCartney, and I would probably have her minced in a wholemeal burger bun, with mayonnaise and salad on the side. And fries. And a thick shake."

YOU ARE THE CHEF

Which star would YOU eat, and how would you cook them? Just give us your celebrity recipe and you could win a meal for two in a star-studded West End restaurant!

Imagine you are stranded on a snow covered mountain side, surrounded by all your favorite stars. The aeroplane was carrying a gas cooker in the hold, and you have a limitless supply of propane gas and clean water. You also have all the cooking utensils you could require, and other ingredients such as flour, butter, salt etc. are available from a nearby shop.

A-TEAM

Tell us which star you'd like to have for dinner, and jot down your recipe on a sheet of paper. Send it to Cook A Star Competition, Viz, P.O. Box 1PT, Newcastle upon Tyne, NE99 1PT. We'll be asking a top TV chef to judge your entries, and if he refuses we'll do it ourselves. The winner will receive first class train travel to London, overnight accommodation in a top hotel, and a meal for two in a top West End restaurant popular with the stars.

CHEAP

Any top London restaurants popular with the stars who are a bit thin on reservations please get in touch at the same address. And if there's any cheap hotels in need of a bit of business drop us a line.

Come to... Peters & Lee Land

Just off the A52

Sammy Davis lives twice...

THUNDERBILL!

Grimsby magistrates heard yesterday how American singer Sammy Davis Junior was alive and well and living on a secret volcanic island in the Pacific ocean from where he plans to take over the world.

'For Your Eye Only' invoice causes storm in Pacific

That was the claim made by unemployed builder Roger Blenkinsop, who appeared before the town's magistrates charged with burglary after a stolen generator was found by police in outbuildings at his home in Cedar Drive, Cleethorpes.

FINE

But the court was unimpressed by Blenkinsop's story and handed him a £250 fine together with a 6 month suspended jail sentence. They also imposed an additional £20 fine for contempt of court after Blenkinsop claimed he took the machine from Mr Davis Junior's secret island after the singer had refused to settle an outstanding bill for £1,200.

CHAMPION

Outside the court yesterday a disappointed Mr Blenkinsop continued to argue his innocence and warned reporters that Sammy Davis Junior, who was thought to have died several years ago, ultimately plans to take over the world from his secret headquarters in a converted volcano. And he blasted stubborn magistrates who refused to visit the area in a helicopter to enable him to prove his innocence.

DANDY

Blenkinsop claims that he was approached by Davis Junior after he had advertised his services as a general builder in a Cleethorpes newsagent's window.

BEANO

"I had a phone call from a man calling himself Mr Glass Eye and I agreed to meet him at an extinct volcano on a small secret island somewhere in the Pacific. The minute I saw him I realised that he was in fact the singer Sammy Davis Junior, and that he must have faked his death and gone to live on this island.

SPARKY

He told me he had various building jobs that needed doing, including converting the volcano into a secret rocket launching pad and installing laboratories, lifts

Davis Junior - escaped in mini submarine

and a mono-rail system. He also wanted a swimming pool built, full of sharks.

TOPPER

Glass Eye's no expense spared shopping list also included:

● A DOZEN nuclear war heads for destroying the world's capital cities.

● A MILLION diamonds for deflecting the sun's rays and focusing them on military installations, plus

● 2000 orange boiler suits.

Indeed, money appeared to be no object for the maniac former all round entertainer. Blenkinsop even overheard a telephone conversation in which the would-be international super villain offered TV's Jeanette Kranky £200,000 a year to act as his evil midget accomplice with a razor sharp hat. An offer which, to the pint sized star's credit, she declined.

BOWLER

Blenkinsop successfully quoted to fit sliding doors to the top of Glass Eye's secret volcano at a cost of £1200, and carried out the work the following week. But two months and several reminders later, there was still no sign of payment from Mr Davis Junior.

"It was obvious that he had no intention of paying, so I decided to go round to his island and demand my money. I burst into his control centre and went straight

up to him and gave him a bit of my mind. But it wasn't until I accidentally stood on his pet cat that I realised I had in fact been talking to Huggy Bear out of Starsky and Hutch, alias seventies actor Antonio de Fargas, who had been recruited by Sammy Davis Junior to act as his expendable double.

SLIP

I turned round to look for the real Glass Eye only to see him disappearing into the sea in a mini-submarine. I was furious, so I loaded the generator into the back of my van in an attempt to recoup some of my losses." The following morning police found the generator at Mr Blenkinsop's home following a burglary at a nearby building site.

SHORT LEG

One condition or Mr Blenkinsop's employment with Davis Junior was that he promise not to tell anyone about his secret island, or of his plans to rule the world. But faced with an unpaid bill for £1200 plus VAT, plus a charge of buglary, Blenkinsop decided to break his vow. And now he fears for his life, convinced that Davis Junior is seeking a deadly reprisal.

"Just this morning I was nearly attacked by a lesbian with a pointy shoe, and on my way into court two sexy birds in bikinis almost done judo on me. I should be given police protection".

LICENSE TO BILL: Blenkinsop's invoice (left), from Cleethorpes with love.

Roger Blenkinsop	General Builder
To Mr Glass Eye Pacific Island	52 Cedar Drive Cleethorpes

INVOICE	11/10/92
To make and install sliding volcano doors (two of) on secret island, and making good.	
Materials	180.00
Transport	20.00
Labour	1,000.00
Total	£1,200.00

In April 1987 Mr Blenkinsop was convicted of stealing lead from the roof of a dissused hoted in Hull despite his protestations that sixties balladeer Matt Monroe, using the alias Silver Thumb, had been using a secret penthouse above the building as the headquarters for a plot to hold the planet Earth to ransom.

On that occasion he was fined £125 and ordered to pay £30 costs and bound over to keep the peace for 6 months.

Sammy Davis Junior (above) as his fans remember him.

GLASS EYE'S SECRET LAIR

Inside the converted volcano which Davis Junior is using as his top secret base. It is from here that the celebrated tap dancer will launch his plan to conquer the world.

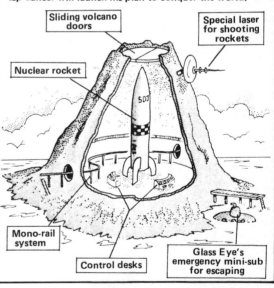

Sliding volcano doors

Special laser for shooting rockets

Nuclear rocket

Mono-rail system

Control desks

Glass Eye's emergency mini-sub for escaping

The MODERN PARENTS

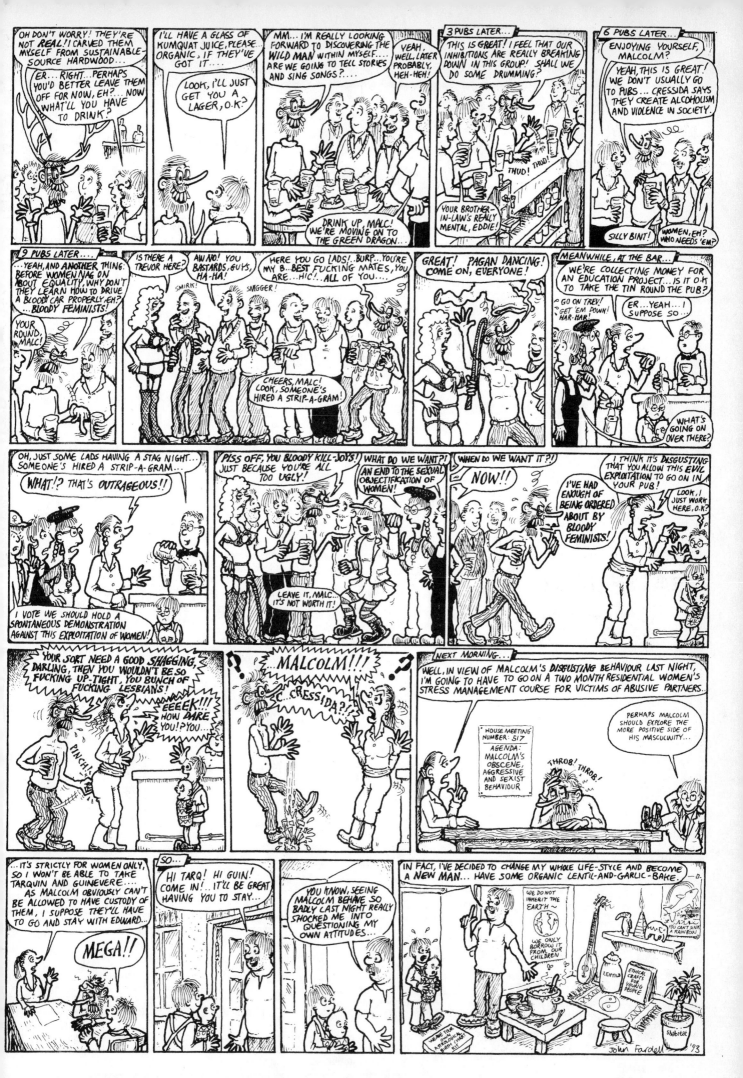

TV NOEL RUINED MY LIFE

While TV millionaire Noel Edmonds was last week signing a £2 million contract to keep him at the BBC, hundreds of miles away one former fan of the star was choking back tears as she recalled how the heartless House Party host left her life in tatters.

The smiling face of cash magnet Noel posing for a publicity photograph outside his bank yesterday

TV NOEL SCORES
Noel netts £10 million

CRINKLEY BOTTOM OBSERVER
NOEL NOEL BBC NOELNOELNOE

Heartless star breaks fans heart in two

Sun star gazer Morgan

Bitter Tyneside mother-of-two Susan Patterson won't be tuning in to any of Noel's new TV shows. For she knows the real Noel Edmonds – the man who TV viewers never get to see.

HEART

For many years ago Susan's heart was broken by her idol Edmonds, then presenter of TV's Swap-shop.

Susan was just a teenager when, along with friends, she went on a day trip to the Lake District. She could hardly believe her eyes when she saw Edmonds in a pub car park.

CLOUT

"He was on his way into the pub and I asked him for his autograph. He said I could have it later, when he came out", Susan recalled, the pain of the memories etched on her face.

Susan waited. And waited.

But Edmonds never returned.

BANGLES

Husband Michael has tried to help Susan rebuild her life, but it has been difficult. At times both have turned to drink, especially at Christmas parties. And as Edmonds' TV career goes from strength to strength, Susan struggles to get by as a part-time receptionist

while Michael looks for work abroad.

"The strange thing is that my two young children both watch TV, and are both big fans of his House Party programme. One day, when they're old enough to understand, I'll tell them about the real Noel Edmonds. The Noel Edmonds who broke my heart", said Susan yesterday.

What the expert says

We spoke to Celebrity expert Piers Morgan of The Sun newspaper and asked him whether Edmonds was within his rights to refuse a young fan an autograph in a pub car park in the Lake District several years ago.

"There are no hard and fast rules governing celebrities in these situations", he told us, "although there are certain recommended standards which celebrities ought to maintain.

I believe Edmonds was heartless to turn down this young girl's request".

SLITS

Has a star ever shat on you from a height? Are you a faithful fan who's been treated like shit by his or her idol? Write and tell us. There's a crisp tenner for every letter we use, and a selection of your best stories appear on the following page.

PRINCE OF WHALES

He parlez with plants – and he talks to the trees. And now Britain's pottiest Prince is doing a Dolittle!

For Buckingham Palace officials have significantly failed to deny rumours that Prince Charles plans to turn his back on Britain and live underwater – becoming the world's first fish monarch.

PRINCE

Close friends of the Prince fear that he intends to submerge himself entirely in water, blow bubbles out of his mouth, and swim about with long, thin trails of excrement dangling out of his arse.

Experts are linking the Prince's dramatic transformation to a 'King Arthur' style experience Charles may have had during a holiday in Cornwall. There is speculation that whilst fishing the heir to the throne witnessed a mysterious fish or something emerging from the water. And it said something to him. And from that moment on he has devoted his life to ruling an underwater kingdom of fish. Probably.

Naval experts believe that the Prince may use a 'Stingray' style submarine in which to travel underwater. And Britain's top shipyards yesterday confirmed that if Buckingham Palace asked them to build a 'Stingray' style submarine, they would be eager to tender for the work. The cost of such a vessel would depend on the Prince's exact specifications, but one source yesterday revealed that it could run into **BILLIONS** of pounds.

Britannia rules the whales: This is how Charles would look with a Troy Tempest hat on (left) and 'Stingray' (below).

A cheaper alternative could be a 'Thunderbird 4' style underwater mini-sub, which would be yellow, and would have attachments on the front. However, Charles' advisors would no doubt

inform the Prince that such a vessel would need to be carried in a 'pod' – a large, transportable container – belonging to Thunderbird 2, which is piloted by Virgil Tracey. Who is a puppet.

'Stingray' jobs boost for North

A North MP yesterday welcomed news that local shipbuilders Swan Hunter may be invited to tender for a 'Stingray' style submarine possibly being built for the Prince of Wales.

"With empty order books job prospects are grim for the remaining workforce", said Labour's Derek Twatt. "Any prospect of new work in the pipeline has got to be good news for the region".

GOOD NEWS

Meanwhile there was more good news for jobs in the region last night when a local shopkeeper announced that he is

By our Chief Industrial Correspondent
TODD BOLLOCKS

to pay a man £25 to do some welding on the sills of his car in order to get it past its MOT.

BLACK MAGIC

Sid Williamson, owner of a second hand shop in the Heaton area, told us he had offered someone £20 to carry out the work, but had now agreed a price of £25.

"It's just the sills that need doing", he told us yesterday. "Otherwise the car is sound as a pound".

You miserable bastards!

Stars shit on fans from a height

On the previous page we asked you to tell us if you had ever been tret like shit by a showbusiness celebrity. And your letters have been pouring in, painting a pretty grim picture of the stars.

For it appears that a great many of the idols we worship and adore are two-faced rats who wouldn't give their fans the time of day. Here is just a brief selection of some of the stories that you have told.

Brucie 'Didn't do well'

Bob Brown of Fulchester had always been a big fan of Bruce Forsyth, until the day his car broke down on the hard shoulder of the M6 near Lancaster. Bob had a flat tyre, it was pouring with rain, and as luck would have it, he'd forgotten to put a spare in the boot.

MORRIS

It was the middle of the night and there wasn't a car in sight – then suddenly a Morris Marina appeared in the opposite carriageway. "It was going very fast, and there was a lot of spray from the rain on the road. And it was dark. But I got a pretty good look at the driver, and I'm fairly sure it was Bruce Forsyth, or someone who looked a lot like him".

Bob waved desperately trying to attract the attention of the Generation Game host, but Forsyth sped by without so much as slowing down. "I felt as if he'd let me down. I'd watched all his shows, but when it came to the crunch he simply didn't want to know".

We rang Forsyth's agent to get his side of the story. We were put on hold. Two minutes later a girl came on the line. "I'm sorry but Bruce is too busy to talk to you this week", we were told.

EXOTIC

No doubt Bruce was 'too busy' to come to the aid of a faithful fan on that cold, dark windswept night in Lancashire all those years ago. Some things never change.

Shirley she could have helped me

Arthur Jones considered himself Shirley Bassey's number one fan. Until the night he turned to his idol for help in an emergency.

HEAVY

After a night of heavy drinking Arthur had called by Bassey's house at 4am to wish his favourite singer good night. But while reaching for the doorbell he had slipped and cut his head on milk bottles that had been left out on the step. In his confusion he then dropped his car keys down a drain. Unable to get home, he decided to wake Shirley by knocking loudly on her front door. But rather than coming to the injured fan's aid, the heartless singer threatened to call the police if he didn't go away.

"I only wanted to borrow a stick or something so I could get my keys back, and maybe a night-cap or something to send me on my way. But the rotten cow wasn't having any of it", Arthur told us.

BITTER

Indeed the selfish singer did call the police, and Arthur ended up spending the night in police cells. But according to Arthur it was he who had the last laugh. "I pissed in her flowerbed", he fondly recalls.

Esther is best'er the bunch

The caring face of TV's Mr Nice Guy Esther Rantzen

But not all the stars are bad. One reader wrote in to tell us a heart warming tale of a celebrity who did care.

WITS

Bill Rodgers, of Fulchester, was at his wits end when his two year old daughter fell blind and he lost his job all in the same week. In desperation he wrote to That's Life's Esther Rantzen.

"I couldn't believe it. Half an hour later she wrote back donating all of her kidneys to our daughter. It was the best gift anyone could ever receive."

TITS

Esther's selflessness has left the Hearts of Gold host with no kidneys of her own and as a result she must spend 20 minutes each day inflating her own artificial kidneys with a foot pump. But her generosity didn't end there. "The next thing you know she gave our pet rabbit the kiss of life after it had been run over by an ice cream van", said a grateful Bill. And later she turned up at Bill's daughter's first birthday party with a wheelbarrow full of BBC money for the sickly child, plus two watering cans full of diamonds.

SHITS

"Words can never say enough to thank Ester for everything she has done for this family", Bill told us. "She truly has a heart of gold".

Help! I need some money

Fred Johnson, also of Fulchester, grew up in the sixties. A big fan of The Beatles, he bought every record the group made. But 20 years later Fred fell on hard times, and in 1989 he found himself unable to pay his gas bill of over £200.

Fred wrote to millionaire Paul McCartney, his childhood hero, asking if he would pay the bill, plus a few pounds extra towards a coat for Fred's wife who had also been a fan of the group. But McCartney, who ranks among the richest men in Britain, didn't even write back.

"Fans like me have been paying McCartney's gas bills for the last 25 years, but when it comes to putting his hand in his own pocket, he simply doesn't want to know. Well, take it from me, I certainly won't be buying any more of his records. And he knows where he can stick his wife's veggie burgers too", said Fred.

LONG LEGS OF THE LAW

Britain's solicitors are the tallest in the world – and that's official!

A worldwide survey of the heights of people employed in the legal profession revealed that Britain's briefs are head and shoulders above the rest when it comes to tallness.

Yet curiously, Britain is one of the few countries that does not stipulate a minimum height for solicitors. Other countries, among them France,

MINIMUM

Belgium and the United States, have recently introduced minimum height requirements in an attempt to stamp out short solicitors. And in Spain where no height restrictions exist, dwarf solicitors are commonplace, with the average height of Latin legal eagles a meagre four feet eight inches.

Britain's average is a towering six feet four, well ahead of the Dutch in second place at five feet eleven.

AVERAGE

Legal profession height watchers were yesterday unable to explain Britain's baffling lead in the legal tallness stakes. One solicitor we spoke to declined to comment unless we paid him £85 an hour to do so.

STUDENT GRANT

LUNCHTIME IN THE REG HOLDSWORTH BAR...

YOU SEE THAT BAG OF CWISPS — THAT'S YOU THAT IS!

ERM...YOU SEE THIS GWASS — THAT'S YOUR SWIMMING POOL!

ER...

YOU WOULDN'T WET IT WIE!!

?

'ERE — YOU DON'T WANT TO DO IT WIKE THAT — YOU WANT TO DO IT WIKE THIS!

HEY! BAG OF SHITE!

HAAAAR! HAAAAR!

OH-HO! HO!HO!

HA-HA! HA-HA!

NO BUT SERIOUSLY YOU GUYS, I'M REEELLY PISSED OFF RIGHT.

WHAT ITH IT GRARNT?

LOOK. THE LATEST VIZ. THEY'VE PUT IT UP TO ONE TWENTY-FIVE!

ONE TWENTY-FIVE? FACKING HELL VATS VE SAME AS A WOUND OF DWINKS!

AND IT'TH NOT ATH FUNNY ATH IT UTHED TO BE, ITH IT?

NO — AND I'VE BEEN READING IT SINCE THE VERY FIRST ISSUE WHEN I WAS AT 6TH FORM COLLEGE ACTUALLY. AND LOOK AT THIS — BIFFA BACON'S ON THE COVER, AND HE'S NOT EVEN IN IT!

TSCHH.

FANTHY ANOTHER THIGGIE GWARNT?

THANKS.

SMACK!

OOYAH!

ARE YE CALLIN' WOR BIFFA A PUFF?

GAN ON MUTHA! FUCK THE BASTAAD!

GROAN

HEH-HEH!

66

TERRY FUCKWITT

THAT'S ME!

The fuckwitted cartoon character

HNNNNNNGGH!!!

LOOK. I DID A POO-POO IN MY POTTY. CAN I HAVE A SWEETY?

IF YOU WERE TWO YEARS OLD, AND I WERE YOUR FATHER, THEN PERHAPS A SWEET WOULD BE A FITTING REWARD

HOWEVER YOU, TERRY, ARE 27...

AND I AM A LORRY DRIVER WHO HAS JUST HAD TO SWERVE OFF THE ROAD TO AVOID YOU, WRECKING MY LORRY IN THE PROCESS

FUCK ME. SO YOU HAVE

UNDER THE CIRCUMSTANCES I FEEL A SWEET MAY BE TOO GENEROUS A REWARD. I THINK PERHAPS A FIRM BOOT IN THE BOLLOCKS MIGHT BE MORE APPROPRIATE

RIGHT.

A BOOT IN THE BOLLOCKS IT IS THEN!

BOOT!

FUCK ME, READERS! I'VE GOT SHIT FOR BRAINS. AND SORE NUTS.

LATER... I'VE DECIDED TO SHAKE OFF MY FUCK WITTED IMAGE ONCE AND FOR ALL. AND I'M STARTING WITH A NEW HAIRCUT...

I'D LIKE A SENSIBLE HAIRCUT PLEASE. QUITE SHORT. NEAT AND TIDY. WITH A NICE SIDE PARTING

I'D LOVE TO GIVE YOU A HAIRCUT TERRY. BUT THIS ISN'T A BARBER'S - IT'S A D.I.Y. STORE. AND I AM MERELY A CUSTOMER IN THE CHECKOUT QUEUE.

THAT'LL BE £39.99 FOR THE BIG MIRROR

EXIT

OOPS!!

SENSIBLE HAIRCUT INDEED! I'VE BEEN QUEUING HERE FOR OVER 15 MINUTES!

WHAT'S GOING ON?

SOME SORT OF FUCKWITT ON THE TILL APPARENTLY

SHORTLY, IN THE MANAGER'S OFFICE...

TERRY, I AM VERY PLEASED WITH YOUR FIRST DAY'S WORK AT THE 'Q&Q' SUPERSTORE. YOU ARE FITTING IN VERY WELL. TOMORROW IS A SATURDAY - OUR BUSIEST DAY OF THE WEEK - SO WE WILL BE CLOSING ALL BUT ONE OF THE TEN CHECKOUTS.

COMPLAINTS

THIS WILL LEAVE YOU FREE TO DO A VERY IMPORTANT JOB INSTEAD...

NEXT DAY...

I'D LIKE TO BUY THIS ONE, SMALL PLANT POT.

OH... DEAR!

IT HASN'T GOT A BAR CODE ON IT!

STAFF ANNOUNCEMENT. MEMBER OF STAFF FROM GARDENING TO CHECK OUT TWO. MEMBER OF STAFF FROM GARDENING TO CHECK OUT TWO

TERRY. THIS PLANT POT HASN'T GOT A BAR CODE ON IT. COULD YOU GO AND CHECK THE PRICE FOR ME

LATER...

HE WON'T BE LONG

HOURS LATER...

NOW THEN. PLANT POTS... FUCK ME. I'M SURE THEY WERE ROUND HERE SOMEWHERE

LIGHT BULBS... PAINT BRUSHES... I MUST BE GETTING CLOSE...

DRILLS... SANDPAPER... PAINT BRUSHES AGAIN...

HE WON'T BE LONG

EXIT

CRAP

PAINT

TOOLS

MORE TOOLS

STAFF

CD 693 vz61

2 THINGS YOU NEVER KNEW ABOUT *ELECTRICITY*

Whether we're washing our teeth with it, opening our car windows with it or being given huge doses of it in a high security mental hospital, there's no getting away from it. Love it or hate it, electricity is here to stay. But how much do we really know about this mysterious energy that starts our cars and makes our telly's work? Here's a few fascinating facts you probably never knew about electricity. . .

1 Most buildings have an underground electricity supply from the local Electricity Board. But churches get theirs direct from God, via enormous 'electricity conductors' at the top of their steeples.

2 Power stations make electricity. Except Duran Duran's music project 'The Power Station'. They make crap records that sound like Duran Duran with the drums turned up.

3 Another pop group with electrical connections are AC/DC. Their name refers to the electrical abbreviations for Alternating and Direct current.

4 If David Bowie approaches you in the street and says he is "AC/DC", don't worry. He's not confusing his pop identity with that of the heavy metal group. He is merely expressing a dual preference for both heterosexual and homosexual activity.

Bowie yesterday

5 Static electricity is a special kind of electricity which lives in nylon carpets and impresses young children by sticking balloons to walls after you have rubbed them on your jumper.

The obscure reference to Duran Duran at No. 2 hardly justifies this rather large picture

6 When singer Eddie Grant invited pop fans to "rock down to Electric Avenue" with the promise that then he would "take them higher", they probably didn't realise that he was referring to the first street in London to have been lit by electricity.

7 Nor would they have been aware that Electric Avenue is, strictly speaking, not an avenue. It's more of a crescent really.

8 Mazda, the name on millions of lightbulbs (as well as a few crap cars) is in fact the name of the Hindu God of light.

9 And Toshiba is the Hindu God of television.

10 In a recent TV advertising campaign Cilla Black told us that a series of biscuit tins filled with house bricks and wired into the mains was a better way of heating a house than a gas central heating system, and all for £2 a week.

11 An electric bill is not a battery operated policeman (although batteries do have copper tops). It is in fact a demand for money from the local Electricity Board, upon receipt of which you realise that Cilla Black was talking out of her arse.

12 And electric blankets are not blankets that run on electricity.

13 Erm. . .

14 Actually they are.

15 Electricity is dangerous. Indeed, it can kill. In fact, it was the only thing that could kill TV puppet Captain Scarlet in the series of the same name.

Captain Scarlet – indestructible

16 Captain Black had already been killed, and had subsequently been taken over by the Mysterons.

Captain Black – already dead

17 There are two types of electric chair. One is a battery powered wheelchair for the elderly or infirm. The other is used by the authorities in America to kill black people.

18 In his sixties hit 'Mellow Yellow' Donovan expressed a belief that "electrical bananas" were going to be "the very next thing".

19 He was about as far wide of the mark as Clive Sinclair in the seventies who thought that an electrical oversized roller skate called the Sinclair C5 was going to be the very next thing.

20 Still, they both had more sense than Gary Numan in the eighties who sang "Are friends electric" while pretending to be a fucking robot, for Christ's sake.

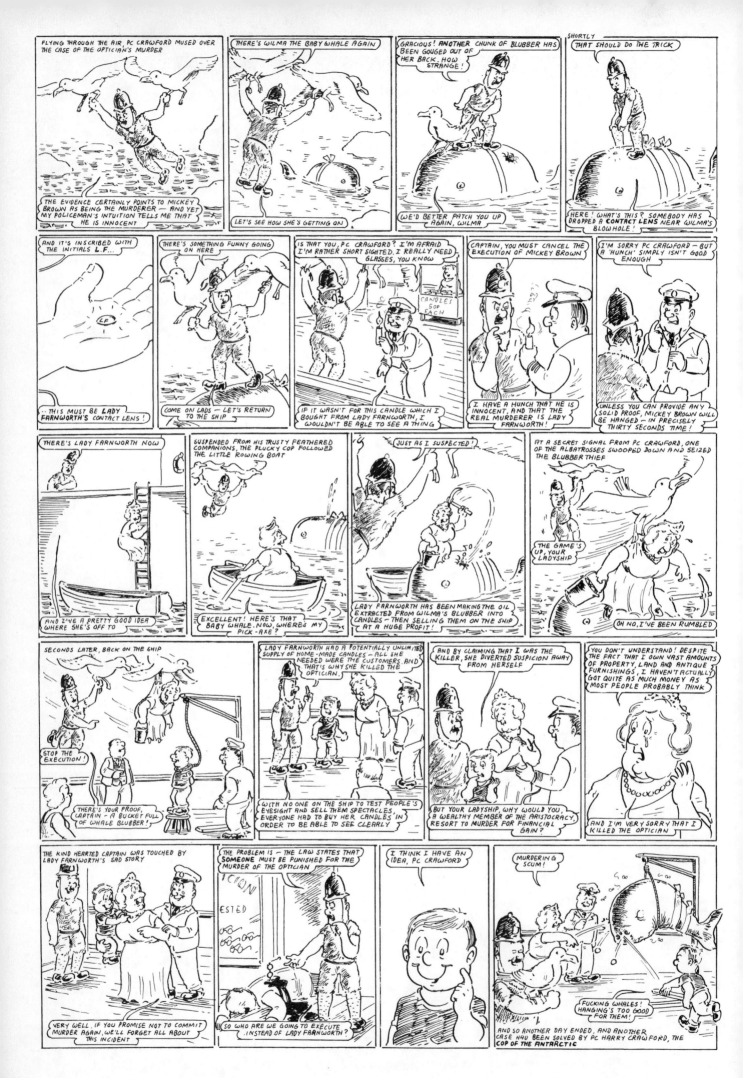

72

New Neptune 'space breasts' theory divides astrologers

PLANET OF THE TITS

By our new Science Correspondent
CLODAGH RODGERS

Space men of the future could be in for a treat when they eventually set foot on the planet Neptune. For new evidence would seem to suggest that the planet's surface is completely covered in large women's breasts.

And rather than 'one small step for a man', it could be a case of 'lots of enormous knockers for everyone', as the first pictures of the planet appear to indicate giant bosoms the size of dustbins.

JUNK

So says amateur astrologer Cedric Herringbone, who has spent the last twenty years gazing into space through a telescope which he bought in a junk shop. "I have been monitoring Neptune for several months, and on a clear night you can just make out the giant tits, all wobbling about as the planet orbits the Sun."

"Of course Neptune is hundreds if not thousands

of miles away from the Sun, and so it is a lot colder than Earth. As a result the space nipples on the planet surface are all hard, and standing up. Like organ stops'.

DINGHY

But the science world has been slow to acknowledge Mr Herringbone's theory, and indeed there are some

space experts who disagree, among them baggy clothes, funny eye TV space boffin Patrick Moore.

CATAMARAN

"I have come across many such theories in my time, such as the Bell Ends of Pluto, and the famous Moon Fannies. But none of

these have ever been proven, and I tend to prefer the theory that planets are made out of space rock, with lots of craters on them, like in The Clangers".

CANOE

Cedric Herringbone is no stranger to controversy. In 1989 he made headlines

Mr Herringbone (centre) with his powerful space telescope. Astrolomer Moore (left) - he poo poos space tits. And the planet Neptune (above) as it appears to the human eye.

when the second hand bookshop he owns was raided, and several boxes of pornographic material were confiscated. On that occasion he received a formal caution after police officers discovered his telescope pointing into a neighbour's bathroom window.

LULU TO GET VISITOR CENTRE

The Queen is to open a new Lulu visitor centre in the autumn, built at a cost of over £250,000.

The centre, which is being jointly funded by Lulu and the Tourist Board, will provide much needed restaurant facilities, a picnic area, an information kiosk and toilets for the estimated 7,000 people who visit Lulu each year.

BARGE

A spokesman for Lulu said that the new centre would provide much needed facilities for fans who had previously had to simply ask for an autograph, make nervous small talk and then go home. "This development will make Lulu a world leader in terms of on-site facilities. And we hope by next year to be going ahead with a car parking scheme for Lulu that will cater for 35 cars".

KAYAK

Lulu is the first British star to open a purpose-built visitor centre, although a Craft Shop, selling woollen jumpers, pottery and ethnic

EXCLUSIVE

Free parking planned for 35 cars

jewellery was opened in 1979 at Michael Parkinson. This was extended at a cost of £14,000 in 1985 to include a small cafe with seating for 14.

Ambitious plans for a multi-million pound Trevor McDonald exhibition centre, hotel and conference facility, due for completion by 1996, have been shelved only days before construction work was due to begin at the popular newsreader.

FNARR

The scheme, which was to have included a 10,000 seat indoor arena, swimming pool and leisure club, was dropped in the light of speculation surrounding the future of ITN's flagship programme The News At Ten.

Parkinson - Craft shop with small cafe

Billy the Fish

AFTER A DRAMATIC HUMAN CANNONBALL STUNT GOES DISASTROUSLY WRONG, MICK HUCKNALL OUT OF SIMPLY RED IS LYING UNCONSCIOUS IN THE ZOO AND ABOUT TO BE EATEN BY MONKEYS. MEANWHILE - THE COUNT IS STILL ON TO DECIDE IF READERS HAVE SENT IN ENOUGH 20ps TO END THIS SERIAL FOR EVER.

WOW BOSS THIS ONE FRAME EPISODE IS A BIT OF A COMEDOWN FROM OUR USUAL TWO-PAGE EXTRAVAGANZAS.

YES BILLY.

IS THIS THE LAST EPISODE? DON'T MISS THE NEXT EPISODE TO FIND OUT.

LETTERBOX

Put these killers on ice

The liberals complain that if we brought back hanging, innocent people could be wrongly executed. The solution is simple. After being hanged the bodies could be put in a fridge, like Walt Disney. If they were later found to be innocent, they could then be brought back to life, using electricity.

D. Marshall
Leytonstone

I was bitterly disappointed when Ford decided to name their new car the 'Mondeo', breaking with the popular trend of naming them after adult 'wank' mags, like Fiesta and Escort. I had hoped to see a new Ford Razzle, or a Ford Readers' Wives Bums Special

Stan Drews
St Andrews

It would be a nice gesture if millionaire TV presenters like Noel Edmonds offered to pay something towards the cost of the electricity which I use every week watching their programmes. Why should I be left to pick up the entire bill when I already fork out every year for a TV licence?

Mrs Edna Richards
Shoreditch

I must admit, since British Rail changed the colour of their trains and started referring to passengers as 'customers', I've completely forgotten what an abysmal and over priced service they provide.

T. Lock
Liverpool

LetterBocks
Viz Commick
P.O. Box 1 PT
Newcasle upon Tyne
NE99 1PT

In reply to Mr F. Ish's letter (Viz 60), I for one vote for a picture of Catherine Zeta-Jones in a bra. Who wants to see a bloke kissing some scrubber's arse again. We watched the tory party do that for years.

Mike Crimlis
Southend

It was a close run race, but Catherine just managed to pip the bloke kissing the bird's arse by the slimmest of margins – one vote to nil. So here she is.

I will read with interest Mr Lomax's letter (Viz, this issue) regarding lager commercials. I personally am a fan of the clever Guinness adverts, with their challenging visual imagery, their air of illusion, and the maturity and mystique which actor Rutger Hauer provides. If I have one criticism it is that they fail to mention that Guinness turns your shit to treacle.

P. McMurphy
Derby

The page that has ten pints and a curry, then shits its pants.

I can't manage on my pension. I fought in two world wars and had an outside toilet etc.

Mrs R. Taylor
York

Holsten Piss off

If American actor Jeff Goldblum is really as clever as he appears to be in those commercials, why is he always drinking piss?

G. Lomax
Sudbury

'There's no substitute for the real thing', my husband said yesterday. He was the manager at a celebrity football match, and the popular seventies soul band had just limped off injured with all the subs already on the pitch. Do I win £5?

Mrs B. Liar
Berkshire

They do a great job

I'm sick of people putting down the Royals. They do a great job, and I for one don't mind paying £6 to look around one of their houses, despite having paid for the cunt already out of my taxes. If I have one criticism (which I don't) it is that perhaps some of the Royal family's enormous wealth could be spent on a toothbrush and some toothpaste for the Queen Mum.

E. Walker
Preston

The Government proposes to invest millions of pounds in complex electronic equipment to facilitate the automatic payment of tolls by drivers using our motorways. Would it not be cheaper and more practical to employ the system successfully operated on fairground dodgem cars for many years, and simply pay tattooed youths to clamber from one car to another demanding a cash payment from the driver.

E. Bainbridge
Walthamstow

They say that an area of rain forest equivalent to the size of Wales is dug up every day. If its that easy, why don't they simply dig up Wales? It would only take a day, and in its place they could build a car park for people visiting Cheshire.

I. Alerstone
Nantwich

In reply to P. Oxley's request for a picture of a puffin (Viz, issue 60), here is a picture of a puffin.

Laura Pottinger
Hove, East Sussex

Well done Laura, who pipped several other puffin spotters to the post. There's a crisp tenner on its way to you – unless the postman gets it first.

I think the Maastricht treaty is a great idea. It's about time Britain started taking orders from randy foreigners who spit while they talk, don't pull their weight during world wars, sleep through half the working day and set fire to sheep.

Mr Z. Allors
Haringey

Hey! What about us?

It's all well and good for the medal grabbing soldiers out in Bosnia who get visits from Sam Fox, free phone calls home and free postage. But I've had to pay 24p to send this letter, and The Sun never bothers to send any fanny out here.
How about some letters and pictures from horny Viz readers instead. Preferably girls.

SPR Collier
Holdfast Camp RE
4 Sqn BELIZE
BFPO 12

£1.25. It's a disgrace. Viz isn't as funny as it used to be, etc.

Peter Morgan
Stoke-on-Trent

Many thanks for other similar letters we received. Unfortunately there is not room to print them all.

On a sunny afternoon last week I was appalled to see young girls basking in bikinis in the park opposite my home. I am 72, and if I wanted to see that sort of filth I would go to a pornographic bookshop.

Mrs D. Groves
Essex

How about a picture of Catherine Zeta-Jones kissing her own arse? I'd happily pay £2 for Viz if you could manage that.

John Kiddle
Truro

Get out of my way

You'd think that after 50 years of shopping some of these pensioners would have made their bloody minds up which way they are going, instead of dawdling around in a daze, changing direction every 2 yards.

L. J. Nelson
Stockton

The other day my wife asked me to remove a scary beetle from the bathroom mat. Imagine my surprise when I discovered it wasn't an inch long insect with ten legs but George Harrison wearing a Frankenstein mask.

Al Aska
St Ives

«TOP TIPS»

SAVE on charity donations by spending a pound on clothes in a charity shop, then selling them for 50p to another charity shop. This way you can give twice as much, at half the cost. I think.

Mr A. Parker
Notts.

FOOL next door into thinking you have more stairs than them by always banging your feet *twice* on each stair.

C. B.
Sedgefield

ALTER the temperature of your bath by alternately adding varying amounts of hot and cold water. But remember that their will always be an overlying downward trend in the temperature.

B. Yeats
Crawley

A LARGE sheet of polystyrene placed on your car roof and trimmed to shape makes and ideal 'all weather' snow covering with which to baffle fellow motorists.

Steve Murphy
Gloucester

AVOID peak hour congestion between Stirling and Glasgow at the A80 Auchinkilns roundabout by taking the A8011 through Cumbernauld and rejoining the A80 beyond this bottleneck.

G. Keddie
Glasgow

STUDENTS. Emphasise your 'individuality' by all wearing identical fucking ridiculous 'far out' clothes while talking loudly in pubs as if you're some kind of bloody authority on life despite the fact that you still haven't left school at the age of 21 and you can't handle your subsidised drink which, incidentally, I bastard well paid for out of my taxes, thankyou very much.

E. Newton
Newton-le-Willows

MUMS. Slip small coloured plastic beads into your kids food so as to easily identify their stools at a later date, should the need to do so arise.

E. Reid
Ely

OLD contact lenses make ideal 'port holes' for small model boats.

F. Johnson
Seaham

BATTENBURG cake, cut into 16 slices and arranged into a square, makes an ideal emergency chess board.

Graham Carter
Ashford, Middlesex

IF YOU feel someone is taking an unreasonable length of time to answer the phone, punish them by putting the receiver down the minute they eventually answer.

Ben Collins
Sunderland

PAUL DANIEL'S ABBACADABRA!

TV's top magician Paul Daniels, assisted by the lovely Debbie McGee, has been up to his naughty tricks again with seventies pop group Abba. This time, using slight of hand, he has replaced one of their heads with that of another pop star and ex-Beatle. Can you spot the odd one out, and name that Beatle? Send your answers on a postcard to Paul Daniels (assisted by the lovely Debbie McGee) Abbacadabra Beatle spotting Competition, Viz, P.O. Box 1PT, Newcastle upon Tyne, NE99 1PT. We'll put all the correct entries into a hat, and the lucky winner drawn out on 31st May 1993 will receive our magical Abba prize – every single Abba record in stock at our local Asda supermarket (providing its open on the 31st, 'cos its a bank holiday). But it probably is. And two lucky runners-up will each receive a tape out of their bargain clearance cassette bin. So hurry up and get those entries flooding in.

OH, LORDY...IT'S THE **FAT SLAGS**

EEH! I LOVE COMIN' ON ME SUMMER HOLS, ME

I LOVE COMIN' ANYTIME... ...NA-AA-AA

MIND YOU, IT'S A PITY THAT Y'CAN'T SUNBATHE TOPLESS WITHOUT BLOKES GOZZIN AT Y' TITS ALL THE TIME...

...LOOK AT 'EM ALL

AYE! FUCKIN' PERVERTS

AH! I'VE FOUND YOUR TROUBLE, LADIES! YOU'VE RUN OUT OF PETROL

ERM...I'LL...ER..JUST TOP YOU UP

WILL Y'NOW? AIN'T Y' BETTER FIX THE CAR FIRST? NA-AA-AA!

DON'T WASTE Y'TIME ON 'IM, TRAY. I BET HE COULDN'T FILL A MOUSE'S EAR

NAH! BUT I KNOW A MAN WHO CAN

'ELLO THERE, LADIES

BAZ!

WHERE ARE Y' OFF TO?

SMUTLINS 'OLIDAY CAMP! I'VE GORRA CHALLET FOR A WEEK

US AN' ALL

SO...

EEH! I LOVE 'AVIN' SOMETHING BIG THROBBIN' BETWEEN ME LEGS

ME AN' ALL AND I LIKE BEIN' FUCKED

NA-AA-AA AA-AA-AA

SMUTLINS 15 MILES

WELCOME TO SMUTLINS

HERE WE ARE, GIRLS

SHORTLY...

C'MON, SAN! GET Y' COZZIE ON...WE'RE GOIN' T' THE POOL

SO...

OOH, LOOK! THEY'VE GOT ONE OF THEM SLIDES

BAGSY FIRST SHOT

PUFF...PANT...FUCK ME...PUFF...YOU'D THINK THEY'D HAVE A...PUFF ...LIFT PUT IN

GASP!

SORRY, LADIES! IT'S CHILDREN ONLY ON THE SLIDE

WELL WE'RE ONLY THIRTEEN, AREN'T WE TRAY, EH!?

AYE! WE'VE JUST GOT BIG TITS FORRUZ AGE

GUMPH!!

C'MON, SAN. RACE Y'T' THE BOTTOM

WHEEEE!!

YEEEE-HAA!

SPLOSH!

77

W.C. 2000 A.D.

While toilet technology has moved slowly forward during the twentieth century, our attitude towards 'the smallest room' has remained routed firmly in Victorian times.

However a revolution is set to take place in unsuspecting water closets all over Britain. And soon, our lavatories will be entering the computer age. Indeed, by the year 2000, the toilet as we know it, will be a thing of the past.

Join us then, on a jour-ney into the future. Come with us into the toilet of tomorrow. And see how technology is set to change our toilet habits for good.

By our Toilets Editor
MIDGE URE
out of Ultravox

'Glittery farts and silver winnits'

Scientific stools glide out out of a luxurious hovering bottom to be 'beamed' away to the Moon. Is this the toilet of tomorrow?

THE SHAPE OF STOOLS TO COME

Looking at them, its pretty hard to believe that the Italians invented toilets. But they did, for it was of course the Romans who introduced lavatories to Britain. Prior to that, people simply had to go out of the window.

But the high technology toilet of the 21st Century would be un recognisable to any Roman in search of the loo. Because to begin with, toilets will no longer be locked away in a quiet corner of the house, or banished to the back yard. Instead they will sit alongside settees, TVs and coffee tables in our living rooms. Or in the kitchen, next to the cooker.

Hygiene

That's because toilet hygiene will be a thing of the past. New healthy vegetarian diets, with plenty of fruit juice and nuts, will mean an end to smelly stools. Instead our bodies will produce odour free motions, similar in texture to Weetabix.

Goodbye Sam

Gone will be the uncertainty about how big our stool will be. Because advances in computer graphics will enable us to design each one ourselves using a mouse and a computer screen connected to our rectum. Not only will we dictate the exact size and shape, but we can even select the colour from a choice of over 500 alternatives.

Hello Samantha

If you find toilet tissue in the bathroom in the year 2000, hold onto it. For it will be a rare and valuable antique. Instead of slaving away wiping our bottoms with fragile strips of tissue paper, in the year 2000 one wipe with a futuristic sheet of silver foil will clean your cleft more thoroughly than you could ever have imagined. Space age winnits – small silver balls like you get on top of Christmas cakes – will disappear instantly. For silver foil loo paper will be coated with special chemicals that not only clean you bum, they'll also cure piles.

Folk

By the year 2000 the stench of urine will be nothing more than a fond memory shared by old folk. For instead of liquid, in the year 2000 we will piss tablets. Two yellow ones normally, or a pink on if we've been eating pickled beetroot.

The toilet of the future will look nothing like the cumbersome, old fashioned things we sit on today. There'll be no toilet seats to begin with. Instead hover rays will suspend our bottoms above a large circular light panel on the floor. Instead of farting, our bottoms will emit small glittering clouds of gas accompanied by dreamy music like on Star Trek. Our stools or piss pills will then appear on the panel below.

Morris

There'll be no chains to pull in the 21st Century toilet. Instead we'll pull up our trousers and walk over to a control console. By sliding one knob up and another one down, our ablutions will be dematerialised, rematerialising seconds later at a sewage works on the moon.

Public toilets will benefit from new techology too. Special X-ray walls will mean no hiding places for dirty old men. And to prevent vandalism a special computer will monitor your bladder and your rectum, to make sure that only people who genuinely need the toilet are allowed in. Payment will also be handled by computer. Simply press your buttocks up against a panel by the door, and the toilet's computer will identify your unique bum print, and charge your visit to your credit card.

Coal

However, some things will never change. And in Harrods department store the faithful toilet attendant will still be there in the year 2000. But tipping him could prove a costly business, due to inflation. For before you leave you will be expected to drop at least £5,000 into his little saucer – the equivalent of 20p in today's money.

B-flat

Sadly, the advent of the space age lavatory will mean an end to one of Britain's best loved traditions. For 'toilet humour' has owed its popularity over the years to our childish obsession and prudish attitudes towards the lavatory. But in the year 2000 Britain's toilets will no longer be taboo. 'Adult humour' magazines will long since have gone to the wall, and words like 'hairy bollocks' will be part and parcel of the English language, no longer the source of any amusement.

BLASPHEMY!

A controversial author yesterday warned that his new book was set to make 'The Satanic Verses' look like a kids' fairy tale.

For Arthur Pilkington claims that in his first novel 'Devil Arse Spunk' God shags a chicken up the back passage. And he fears that it may result in a Salman Rushdie style fatwa being put on him by the Church of England. Indeed, he has already sent a copy to the Archbishop of Canterbury, and he fears the official announcement of a death threat could be imminent.

"I'm not afraid of controversy", he told us yesterday speaking from a secret address where he has been in hiding for several days. " I have already written to Melvyn Bragg asking for his support, and I am trying to arrange a meeting with the Prime Minister so that I can bring attention to my plight."

Mr Pilkington hopes that his book will repeat the success of Salman Rushdie's highly controversial best seller, although as yet no publisher has been found. "At the minute there are a few spelling mistakes that need ironing out, and at seven pages it looks a little short. I'm thinking of adding a few bits about Jesus and farmyard animals to try and pad it out a little.

God sex chicken book set to cause a storm

Once I get it typed up properly publishers will be biting my hands off – you just see", he told us.

We rang controversial Christian Cliff Richard to try and obtain a quote that we could use out of context. However, the former singer, who changed his name from Harry Webb when he turned his back on a pop career in the seventies, wasn't in.

FELIX AND HIS EXPENSIVE AMAZING **UNDERPANTS**

I'VE DEVELOPED AN INTEREST IN GIRLS, READERS! SO I'VE INVESTED £20 IN A NEW PAIR OF KALVIN KLIEN UNDERPANTS TO IMPRESS THEM WITH.

HI GIRLS. LIKE MY NEW PANTS?

FAT BERK!

YEAH. WHAT AN ARSEHOLE.

HUMPH! TWENTY QUID AND THEY NEVER EVEN BATTED AN EYELID! WHAT A RIP OFF!

THERE — THAT'S BETTER. I CAN'T GO WRONG IN MY AMAZING UNDERPANTS!

HMMM. THAT FASHIONABLE YOUTH WEARING HIS LAMBSWOOL SWEATER ON HIS SHOULDERS GIVES ME AN IDEA!

HEY GIRLS. WHAT'S HAPPENING?

AAAAAH!

EEEEEK! A FLASHER!

WELL, THAT DIDN'T SEEM TO WORK EITHER.

GIRLS JUST DON'T SEEM TO NOTICE ME. IT MUST BE MY UNDERPANTS.

OH I DON'T KNOW FELIX. PERHAPS YOU ATTACH TOO GREAT A SIGNIFICANCE TO THE ROLE YOUR UNDERPANTS PLAY IN ALL THIS.

MAYBE YOU SHOULD THINK ABOUT TAKING GIRLS OUT. TO THE CINEMA PERHAPS.

YOU'RE RIGHT! I COULD FILL MY UNDERPANTS WITH POP CORN. THAT WOULD IMPRESS THEM!

I GIVE UP.

HELLO, JANE? FELIX HERE. I WONDERED IF YOU'D LIKE TO COME WITH ME TO THE PICTURES TONIGHT.

MY WHAT? YES ... OF COURSE I'LL BE WEARING MY UNDERPANTS. DO YOU...

HELLO? THAT'S ODD. SHE'S HUNG UP.

NEVER MIND. THERE'S PLENTY MORE PEBBLES ON THE BEACH. LET'S SEE NOW...

AND I COULD FILL MY UNDERPANTS WITH POPCORN, OR USE THEM AS A FRIDGE TO KEEP OUR CHOC ICES COLD, OR ...

HELLO? HELLO? OH DAMN, NOT AGAIN!

THAT'S IT. I'M GOING TO GAS MYSELF IN MY UNDERPANTS. I JUST NEED TO FART, THAT'S ALL ...

AH, THERE YOU ARE FELIX. I'M EXPECTING A FROST TONIGHT, SO I'VE BROUGHT THIS LARGE MARROW AND TWO BIG PUMPKINS IN FROM THE GREENHOUSE.

THING IS, I NEED SOMEWHERE TO KEEP THEM.

WELL, YOU COULD ALWAYS POP THEM IN MY UNDERPANTS. THEY'D MAKE A FINE FROSTY WEATHER VEGETABLE INCUBATOR UNIT.

A FEW DAYS LATER...

YES, I'D LOVE TO GO TO THE PICTURES WITH YOU. I COULD FIT YOU IN NEXT THURSDAY. ANY GOOD? OKAY. SEE YOU THEN.

IT'S FUNNY, BUT SINCE I'VE BEEN INCUBATING DAD'S VEGETABLES I'VE HAD DOZENS OF GIRLS ASK ME OUT. I'M BOOKED UP NOW FOR THREE WEEKS SOLID.

PERHAPS IT'S THE SMELL OF VEGETABLES OR SOMETHING WHICH THEY LIKE. WHO KNOWS?

VIZ 61   C.D./LEW STRINGER.

JURASSIC PARK, TIPTON

World's first dinosaur zoo set for West Midlands

Plans are afoot to open the world's first multi-pound real life 'Jurassic Park' at Tipton, in the West Midlands.

Property developer and former Councillor Hugo Guthrie unveiled his plans yesterday at a special press conference. And if his ambitious scheme gets the go ahead, dinosaurs could be returning to Tipton after a million year absence.

Blockbuster

Mr Guthrie admits that the idea came to him after seeing the blockbuster film 'Jurassic Park' at the cinema recently. "Mrs Guthrie and I were most impressed, but we believe Tipton can go one better than Hollywood and create the real thing, here in the West Midlands".

Ballroom Blitz

Experiments to recreate giant dinosaurs, extinct for millions of years, are already well advanced. "We hope that by crossing various existing animals with each other we can bypass the need for revolutionary advances in genetic science. For example, my wife has suggested that by crossing an ostrich with a tortoise and perhaps a frog we could achieve something not unakin to a dinosaur."

Wig Wam Bam

If all goes according to plan Tipton Jurassic Park will open its doors to the public

Hugo Guthrie (left) - the Tipton based visionary behind Jurassic Park, and one of his terrifying creations - a real life dinosaur - which he has bread specially in his garage.

this autumn. "I have already written to Sir David Attenborough who stars in the film, asking him to perform the opening ceremony", Mr Guthrie announced. A site has been chosen on derelict land adjacent to a garden centre belonging to Mr Guthrie's brother-in-law, and the first dinosaurs could be released there as soon as the area has been fenced.

Little Willie

Mr Guthrie's application for a real life dinosaur zoo goes before the town's planning committee next Thursday, and they are bound to weigh up the possible dangers associated with real life dinosaurs against the undoubtable benefits to tourism that such a scheme would offer.

Residents in nearby Walsall have already expressed fears that escaped dinosaurs could pose an additional safety threat to children, on top on the menace already caused by joy riders.

Big Fanny

Last night Mr Guthrie was able to confirm rumours circulating among neighbours that one dinosaur has already been successfully created in a garage adjoining his home in Cedar Gardens. "I am pleased to say that Mrs Guthrie and I have succeeded in crossing a stuffed armadillo with a pine cone to get a small stegosaurus. We are having a few problems with the pine cone falling off at present, but hope to unveil it in the near future".

JURASSIC SHED

By our Gardens & Outhouses Correspondent THE HUES CORPORATION

Scientists in California believe they have discovered the 'missing link' between today's garden sheds, and the tree houses used by monkey's to keep bananas in.

Fossil remains discovered in 'Dinosaur Valley', an area where hundreds of dinosaur bones have been discovered, appear to be those of a primitive cave man garden shed.

Historians shed light on shed history mystery

BRANCHES

Tests show that the structure, which was made of tree branches with large leaves on the roof, probably contained garden tools, although DNA testing has been inconclusive.

TRUNKS

For many years scientists have been baffled by the mystery of shed development, and a vital piece of the historical jigsaw puzzle has always illuded them. Until now the earliest shed

remains on record were those of a Roman shed, containing a bike and a lawn mower, found near the Roman fort of Vindolanda in Northumberland.

TUSKS

Modern sheds, which are made of wood, or aluminum, can be purchased for as little as £99, including erection. Wooden or metal sheds however are not to be confused with outhouses, the latter being of concrete, brick or stone construction.

GOING FOR A SHED

With the late ARTHUR NEGUS O.B.E.

"Think you know your sheds? Well here's a little test for all you armchair shed experts at home. There are four sheds shown below, each from different eras in hut history. Can you date them all? Have a go, then check the answers below. *I may be dead, but when is these shed?*"

1 **2**

3 **4**

ASBESTOS £45 54

'CUNT' TAYLOR MUST HANG

along with his family

An alcoholic sports writer and former third division footballer has called for the death penalty to be introduced for football managers after England's disappointing results in the World Cup qualifying matches.

And John Cobblers has offered to don a black cap and pull the lever himself, claiming that Taylor's family should also face the death penalty, along with anyone else who knows him.

COBBLERS

In a recent editorial Mr Cobblers likened Taylor to a woman's vagina after England's 2-1 defeat in a friendly with the United

States. Under a banner headline which read 'CUNT', Mr Taylor was pictured with a large hairy fanny instead of a nose, and a tampon in his mouth.

"England have not won a game in over two months", Mr Cobblers said yesterday. "The fact that we have not played one is irrelevant. We invented football, yet teams made up entirely of foreigners seem able to beat us at

will. Taylor should hang, and so should his successor."

BOLLOCKS

Mr Cobblers caused a storm of controversy last month when he suggested England cricket captain Graham Gooch should be castrated following two test defeats at the hands of Australia. However, he later withdrew his remark and suggested that Mr Gooch should be crowned King of England after England drew the following game.

The All New
FINBARR SAUNDERS 93

& his SAME AS USUAL DOUBLE ENTENDRES

FOR WANT OF ANY BETTER PLOT, MR GIMLET IS TAKING FINBARR FISHING...

RIGHT. THIS LOOKS LIKE A GOOD SPOT TO SIT DOWN AND GET MY TACKLE OUT.

FNARR! FNARR!

WILL YOU UNFOLD THE PORTABLE STOOLS?

IF YOU OPEN THEIR LEGS REALLY WIDE IT ALL POPS INTO PLACE MUCH MORE EASILY.

K-YAK! K-YAK!

ARF! ARF!

CORRECT USE OF THE FLOAT IS VERY IMPORTANT IN ORDER TO ATTRACT FISH. I LIKE TO DIP THE END IN A FEW TIMES TO GET THEM INTERESTED.

YIP! YIP!

KURK! KURK!

WOOF! WOOF!

YOU MUST ALSO KNOW WHAT TO DO WHEN A FISH BITES.

WHEN YOUR ROD STARTS WOBBLING UP AND DOWN, GRIP IT FIRMLY...

...BUT DON'T TUG ON IT TOO HARD, OR IT MIGHT COME OFF.

LOOK! ON YOUR HOOK! IT'S A SALMON. YOU'VE GOT A BIG ONE! IT'S LONG AND PINK WITH A PURPLE HEAD!

G-YARP! G-YARP!

HURP! HURP!

WELL DONE FINBARR. I DIDN'T REALISE WHAT A WHOPPER YOU'D GOT TILL YOU PULLED IT OUT.

EH?!

HAAAR! HAAAR!

IT'S ALWAYS NICE TO HAVE A POLAROID OF YOURSELF HOLDING IT UP SO EVERYONE CAN SEE WHAT A MAGNIFICENT ONE IT IS.

SQNNK! SQNNK!

WHEN YOUR MOTHER COMES FISHING WITH ME, AND I CATCH ONE, I SOMETIMES LET HER HOLD IT BEFORE I POP IT BACK! MIND YOU, SOME WOMEN DON'T LIKE TO TOUCH THEM WHILE THEY'RE STILL SLIPPERY.

YUK! YUK!

SNIT! SNIT!

YOUR MUM'S NOT SQUEAMISH THOUGH.

I REMEMBER ONE COLD MORNING MY BEST MAGGOT HAD GONE ALL LIMP AND LIFELESS. NO MATTER HOW MUCH I RUBBED IT - IT JUST LAY THERE - ALL PLOPPY.

SO MRS. SAUNDERS POPPED IT IN HER MOUTH AND IT SOON LIVENED UP. THEN SHE TOOK IT OUT AND TOSSED IT INTO THE WATER.

YOUR MOTHER ALWAYS LIKES TO EAT THE LARGER FISH THAT WE CATCH. SHE'S GOT NO TIME FOR SIX-INCH TIDDLERS - BUT ANYTHING OVER FOUR POUNDS AND SHE'LL BE SMACKING HER LIPS IN FRONT OF IT BEFORE BEDTIME.

FLAMP! FLAMP!

GLUCK! GLUCK!

IN FACT, I REMEMBER ONE ENORMOUS ONE SHE CAUGHT WHEN WE WENT TICKLING TROUT. SHE JUST PUT HER FINGERS UNDERNEATH IT AND RUBBED GENTLY. THEN - JUST BEFORE IT SHOT OFF - SHE GRABBED IT FIRMLY JUST BEHIND THE HEAD.

WE TOOK IT HOME TO FRY IT FOR SUPPER - BUT I WHIPPED IT OUT BEFORE IT HAD BEEN IN LONG ENOUGH. THERE WAS BATTER EVERYWHERE.

K-YAARF! K-YAARF!

WHOOP! WHOOP!

YAK! YAK! YAK!

MY FISHING EQUIPMENT CASE IS BROKEN SO I'VE BORROWED MRS. SAUNDERS'S. UNFORTUNATELY SHE'S ALLOWED MY LURES TO BECOME TANGLED I WISH YOUR MOTHER WAS HERE TO UNDO MY FLIES WITH HER NIMBLE FINGERS.

FWA! FWA!

HO! HO!

NOW IT'S TIME TO PACK UP - AND I FEAR THAT THESE SPECIAL STONES I USE TO STUN THE FISH MAY ROLL INTO THE RIVER WHILE I ATTEMPT TO CRAM MY FISHING GEAR INTO THIS PORTMANTEAU.

MRS. SAUNDERS ALWAYS LIKES TO HOLD ONTO MY ROCKS WHILE I'M REPEATEDLY TRYING TO STUFF MY TACKLE INTO HER BOX.

FNURR! FNURR!

HAARR! HAARR!

HI! HI! HI! HI!

YOO! HOO! FINBARR! MR. GIMLET! YOU FORGOT YOUR SANDWICHES!

GREAT! YOUR MOTHER'S ENORMOUS PICNIC LUNCHES ALWAYS ATTRACT THE DUCKS.

ONE LOOK AT THE SIZE OF MY PACKET AND THE BIRDS COME FLOCKING AROUND.

SHORTLY...

OOH MR. GIMLET! IT'S ENORMOUS! I CAN'T GET MY FINGERS ROUND IT!

YES. I BET IT GAVE YOU QUITE A SHOCK.

SOUNDS LIKE MUM AND MR. GIMLET HAVE CAUGHT AN ELECTRIC EEL.

NOW RUB MY TITS.

ETC...

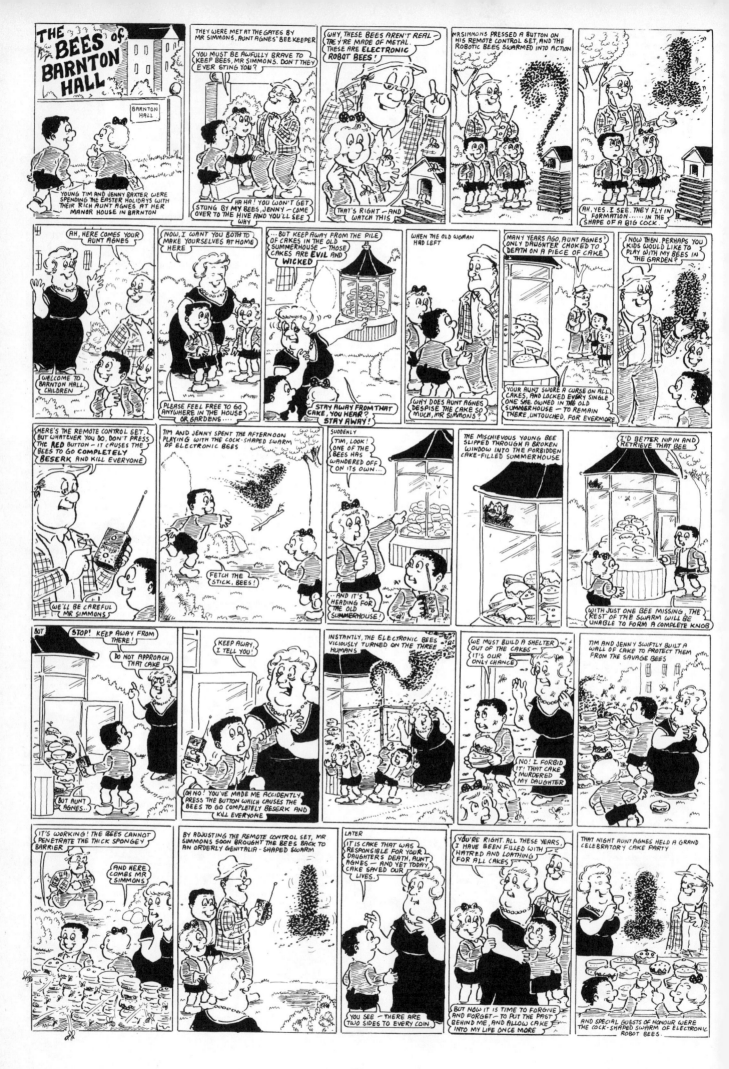

Jack Black
and the
CHINESE BUNTING MYSTERY

Jack Black and his dog Silver had gone to stay with Jack's Aunt Meg at her idyllic country cottage in the Cotswolds.

THEY'RE HAVING A PARTY AT THE LOCAL ORPHANAGE TOMORROW SO I'M GOING OVER THERE TO PUT SOME DECORATIONS UP.

GOSH! CAN SILVER AND I HELP?

WHY OF COURSE YOU CAN. WHY DON'T YOU COME TO THE VILLAGE AND HELP ME CHOOSE SOME BUNTING.

GOSH! I'VE NEVER CHOSEN BUNTING BEFORE. THAT WILL BE FUN!

FIRST I'M GOING TO POP INTO THE CHINESE LAUNDERETTE TO PICK UP SOME TROUSERS I'VE HAD CLEANED.

BUTCHER

Mr Po's
COTSWOLD COUNTRY
CHINESE LAUNDERETTE

Trousers
Cleaned
& Pressed
£1.4/6d
Turn ups FREE

NO TICKY NO SHIRTY

CAN WE GET THE BUNTING NEXT AUNT MEG?

YES, COME ON. MRS GREEN AT THE POST OFFICE USUALLY HAS SOME.

At the Post Office...

HELLO MRS GREEN. DO YOU HAVE ANY BUNTING?

WHY YES MEG. I HAVE TWO TYPES IN STOCK.

THERE'S BRITISH BUNTING, AT HALF A CROWN A FOOT, OR THIS TYPE FOR THRUPPENCE A YARD.

WHY IS ONE SO EXPENSIVE, AND THE OTHER SO CHEAP?

THE CHEAP BUNTING IS MADE IN CHINA, WHERE DIFFERENT WORK ETHICS EXIST TO HERE IN BRITAIN.

WE'LL TAKE SIX YARDS OF THE CHEAP BUNTING PLEASE MRS GREEN.

THAT'LL BE ONE BOB AND A TANNER EXACTLY PLEASE MEG.

BUT AUNT MEG... YOU CAN'T DO THAT. IT'S CHINESE! YOU'RE PRACTICALLY HANDING MONEY TO FOREIGNERS!

I'M SORRY JACK. I SIMPLY CAN'T AFFORD TO DECK OUT THE ORPHANAGE IN BRITISH BUNTING.

Later, at the orphanage...

THERE NOW! THE CHILDREN WILL LOVE THIS.

YES JACK. IT SHOULD BE A GOOD PARTY TOMORROW.

That evening...

I'D BETTER CHECK THAT THESE TROUSERS I PICKED UP FROM THE CHINESE LAUNDERETTE HAVE BEEN PROPERLY CLEANED.

GOOD THINKING AUNT MEG. GENERALLY SPEAKING, YOU CAN'T TRUST FOREIGNERS.

THAT'S PECULIAR! I COULD HAVE SWORN THESE WERE A GENEROUS CRIMPOLENE FLARE WHEN I HANDED THEM IN. NOW THEY'RE DRAINPIPES!

I CAN'T WEAR THESE FOR THE PARTY.

Bright and early the next day Jack, Meg and Silver headed for the orphanage...

GOSH! SMOKE BILLOWING FROM THE ORPHANAGE! THERE MUST BE A FIRE.

A constable greeted them at the gate...

GOODNESS! WHAT HAPPENED OFFICER?

I'M AFRAID THERE HAS BEEN A FIRE IN WHICH ALL OF THE CHILDREN HAVE PERISHED, YOUNG JACK. BUT DON'T WORRY...

MOST OF THEM WERE FROM SINGLE PARENT FAMILIES AND SHOULD HAVE BEEN THE RESPONSIBILITY OF THEIR ABSENT FATHERS. NOT THE STATE.

THAT'S A RELIEF. BUT WHAT STARTED THE FIRE?

IT'S EARLY DAYS YET JACK, BUT WE SUSPECT IT WAS CAUSED BY FAULTY BUNTING.

WE FOUND THIS HANGING FROM A WINDOW FRAME.

SO, THAT'S WHY THE CHINESE BUNTING WAS SO CHEAP. IT'S MANUFACTURERS FLAGRANTLY DISREGARD THE STRINGENT BRITISH SAFETY STANDARDS!

I THINK WE SHOULD PAY A VISIT TO MRS GREEN, SILVER. SHE IS SELLING DEADLY DECORATIONS!

But as they approached the Post Office...

LOOK! MRS GREEN ALREADY HAS A VISITOR. LET'S INVESTIGATE!

CRIKEY! IT'S A MYSTERY CHINA MAN, AND HE'S HANDING MRS GREEN A BOX OF BUNTING!

SO THAT'S IT. AUNT MEG'S MISSING FLARES, THE CHEAP BUNTING... IT'S ALL BEGINNING TO MAKE SENSE. MRS GREEN IS IN CAHOOTS WITH THE CHINA MAN.

HE HAS BEEN SNIPPING TRIANGULAR SECTIONS OUT OF FLARED TROUSER LEGS AND USING THEM TO MAKE HAZARDOUS BUNTING. MRS GREEN HAS BEEN ACTING AS A FENCE, SELLING THE BUNTING ON TO UNSUSPECTING PARTY ORGANISERS.

Presently...

WELL DONE JACK. YOU'VE CRACKED A MAJOR COTSWOLD CHINESE FLARE THEFT AND BUNTING RACKET, RESPONSIBLE FOR THE DEATHS OF SEVERAL ORPHANS.

WHAT WILL HAPPEN TO MRS GREEN? SHE'S BEEN OUR SUB POST MISTRESS FOR OVER FORTY YEARS.

CD/SE 7.93 viz61

SHE'S OLD AND FRAIL AND WON'T SURVIVE LONG IN BRITAIN'S OVERCROWDED JAILS. BUT THAT'S WHERE SHE'S GOING, ALONG WITH OUR CHINESE FRIEND.

AND I'M PERSONALLY RECOMMENDING THAT THEY BOTH SERVE AT LEAST FIFTY YEARS!

WELL, I THINK THIS CALLS FOR A CELEBRATORY PARTY!

YES, AND THIS TIME WE'LL BE BUYING BRITISH BUNTING!

YES JACK. HOORAY FOR BRITAIN!

WOOF! WOOF!

THE END

ROGER MELLIE

THE MAN ON THE TELLY

ROGER HAS BEEN RUSHED TO HOSPITAL SUFFERING FROM CHEST PAINS...

FULCHESTER NUFFIELD HOSPITAL
OUT PATIENTS ▷
CELEBRITY ADMISSIONS
EMERGENCY DEPARTMENT

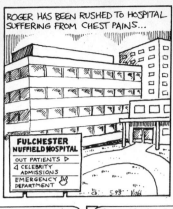

HI ROGER. HOW ARE YOU?

OH, HI TOM. I'M NOT TOO BAD...

BUT I HAVE FELT BETTER

SO WHAT EXACTLY HAPPENED ROGER? YOU'VE GIVEN US ALL QUITE A SCARE

NOTHING LIKE THE SCARE I'VE HAD TOM! I THOUGHT I WAS A GONNA! I THOUGHT THE OLD TICKER HAD PACKED IN ON ME!

I'D JUST HAD A BIG SLAP UP FRIED BREAKFAST ON SATURDAY AND I WAS ON MY WAY TO THE GOLF CLUB WHEN I STOPPED IN FOR A FEW PINTS OF LAGER AT MY LOCAL

SUDDENLY I GOT THIS TERRIBLE PAIN IN MY CHEST. MY LIFE FLASHED BEFORE MY EYES! I THOUGHT THAT WAS IT TOM!

THEY RUSHED ME STRAIGHT IN HERE FOR TESTS

SO WHAT DO THE DOCTORS THINK IT IS?

IS IT SOME SORT OF HEART TROUBLE?

NO. IT WAS **WIND** ACTUALLY. I LET OFF THIS MASSIVE FART IN THE AMBULANCE AND THE PAIN SIMPLY VANISHED!

OH... I SEE.

STANK A BIT MIND. I TOLD THE DOCTOR IT WAS PROBABLY A CURRY OR SOMETHING THAT HAD GOT STUCK, AND CAUSED SOME SORT OF AIR LOCK UP MY SHITTER

MMM... YES.

ANYWAY, I'M GLAD I WENT PRIVATE. THEY'RE LETTING ME STAY FOR A WEEK TO RECOUPERATE, AT £400 A NIGHT.

SO YOU'RE IN GOOD HANDS THEN

NOT HALF! THESE PRIVATE NURSES ARE GAGGING FOR IT! CASH THAT IS. I GET A BED BATH EVERY DAY, AND FOR TEN QUID EXTRA I GET A HAND JOB.

SO WHEN MIGHT WE SEE YOU BACK AT WORK ROGER?

I'M BACK ALREADY

I'M WORKING ON A NEW SHOW THAT'S BEEN INSPIRED BY THE TIME I'VE SPENT IN HOSPITAL. YOU'LL **LOVE** THIS ONE TOM!

IT'S CALLED 'THROUGH THE ARSEHOLE'

WHAT!?!

TAKE IT FROM ME TOM. THIS WILL RUN AND RUN!

ALL WE NEED IS A LENGTH OF OPTIC FIBRE CABLE, THAT STUFF DOCTORS USE TO LOOK INSIDE YOUR TUBES. WE SHOVE IT UP A CELEBRITIES' JACKSIE, AND HEY PRESTO! WE CAN FILM INSIDE THEIR ARSEHOLE!

OUR PANEL OF GUESTS THEN HAVE TO TRY AND GUESS WHOSE RINGPIECE THEY'RE LOOKING UP. IT'S BRILLIANT!!

ROGER! HAVE YOU LOST YOUR SENSES? "THROUGH THE ARSEHOLE" INDEED! THE I.B.A. WOULD NEVER ALLOW IT

OKAY, OKAY...

NO PROBLEM TOM. WE JUST JUGGLE THE FORMAT A LITTLE TO KEEP EVERYONE HAPPY. LET'S SEE...

GOT IT! WE CALL IT "DIRT BOX JURY" AND EVERY WEEK WE FISH ABOUT UP **SIX** DIFFERENT STARS' BACKSIDES. THE JURY HAVE TO LOOK UP EACH BUM, AND CHOOSE THEIR FAVOURITE. THEN THE WINNER TAKES A BUCKET BEHIND A CURTAIN, AND WHILE HE'S THERE THE JURY HAVE TO DECIDE WHETHER IT'LL BE A **SHIT** OR A **PISS**!"

I'LL TELL YOU WHAT TOM. THIS IS ONE FUCK OF AN IDEA! WE'RE TALKING PRIME TIME TELEVISION. THIS WILL PUT ME IN THE NOEL EDMONDS LEAGUE!

HE CAN STUFF HIS 'HOUSE PARTY' UP HIS FUCKING CRINKLEY ARSEHOLE! "DIRTBOX JURY" WILL BE THE SHOW!!!

BUT ROGER, HOW MANY STARS FROM THE WONDERFUL WORLD OF LIGHT ENTERTAINMENT ARE GOING TO VOLUNTEER TO HAVE SOMETHING SHOVED UP THEIR ARSE AND... WRIGGLED.... AROUND... INSIDE... IT. MMMMM!

EXACTLY!

A FEW WEEKS LATER "DIRTBOX JURY" IS LIVE ON THE AIR...

HOLD STILL MR. SLATTERY.

AND NOW LET'S TAKE A LOOK AT DIRT BOX NUMBER SIX

THERE IT IS ON THE MONITOR FOR THE JURY TO TAKE A GOOD LOOK AT.

DIRTBOX JURY 6 5 2

AH, NOW THEN... THIS IS INTERESTING. I THINK WE'VE GOT SOME PILES COMING UP HERE...

THROUGH THE SPHINCTER WE GO AND INTO THE RECTUM. CAN WE MOVE IN A LITTLE FURTHER THERE...

ROGER WAS RIGHT! THE SHOW IS INCREDIBLEY POPULAR! WE'VE ALREADY RECEIVED OVER 500 LETTERS- NOT FROM VIEWERS, BUT FROM STARS DESPERATE TO GET THEIR ARSES ON THE SHOW!

INSIDE THE BRAIN OF A KILLER

By our Crime Reporter GREGG BAKERY

Michael Sams brain, if we saw it in daylight, would not look unlike a cauliflower. But instead of being green, it would be pink, with some grey bits.

Michael Sams' brain is important, because it is the special place where messages from all over his body are received. A network of nerves runs around our bodies, like a system of roads, carrying signals back and forth, to and from the brain. These travel up the spine, through Michael Sams' neck, and into his brain.

CAULIFLOWER

Unlike a cauliflower, the middle of Michael Sams' brain is made up of millions of cells which he uses to think. It was here, in the middle of Sams' brain, that he hatched his evil plot to kidnap estate agents.

KNOB

Michael Sams' eyes are in constant contact with his brain. It was the evil killers' eyes which he used to see victims with, and it was the same two eyes which he used when he swooped to collect ransom money from his kidnap victim at a pre-arranged spot.

COTTAGE

The money was left on a railway bridge by police. Sams would have pointed his eyes at the money in order to see it. An image of the money would then have been focused onto his retina, in the same way that holiday slides are projected onto a slide screen. From the retina at the back of the eye, an optic nerve conveys these pictures into the evil brain of killer Sams.

In a split second, another message is on its way from inside the brain cells, through the bodies' nervous system, to the killers one remaining leg. That message is short and simple. 'Walk towards the money'.

FILCH

As well as thinking, the brain is also busy co-ordinating Sams movements. It arranges for him to bend down when he reaches the cash which is littering the ground in silver bundles. Sams' busy brain then tells the evil killer to pick up the money with his hands.

As he rode home on his moped, Sams would have used his brain to work out the best route to take, when to slow down, turn corners, and stop, etc. Without his brain – the control centre of his evil body – he could never have carried out his kidnap plot.

Killer kidnapper Michael Sams is destined to go down in history as the one legged train spotting murderer, who kidnapped and killed terrified estate agents.

But what evil force can turn a three times married former merchant seaman and moped enthusiast, into Britain's most notorious murderer for at least a year? What goes on inside the mind of a former long distance runner with an IQ of 138 that makes him kidnap, wrongfully imprison and kill?

Here, exclusively, we take you inside the brain of Michael Sams to provide a revealing insight into the mind of a murderer.

What makes a killer tick?

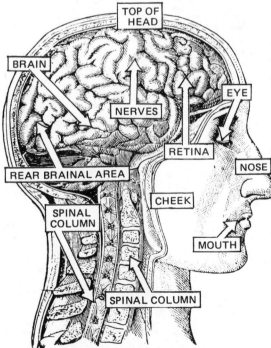

A cross section through a brain similar to that inside the head of evil one legged kidnap killer Sams.

Killer in the corner shop

LIKE OTHER notorious killers before him, including Dennis Neilsen and 'Yorkshire Ripper' Peter Sutcliffe, Michael Sams would have quite frequently used a corner shop to buy food and other groceries.

And other shoppers would have been unaware of the kidnapper in their midst.

Corner shops have traditionally been a part of British life for many years, although recently their future has been threatened by the increasing popularity of larger supermarkets and out of town hypermarkets.

Supermarket

Large retail supermarket chains are able to offer groceries at cheaper prices due to their bulk wholesale buying, and often provide a wider choice of goods. They also offer free car parking.

Okaybazaar

However corner shops survive, as it is often more convenient to nip to a nearby store for essential items than it is to travel to a hypermarket. By staying open late at night, and opening on Sundays, corner shops win extra customers. However shoppers who use their local convenience store, including killers such as Michael Sams, will notice that produce is often more expensive than in larger supermarkets.

This is because a small business such as a corner shop pays higher prices for its stock, and must maintain sufficient profit margin to cover its overheads.

I READ ABOUT EVIL SAMS

Says the model he never met

Shapely Cindy Side-bottom has a figure that would drive men crazy. Her adorable assets have turned many a head as the sexy 19-year-old heads for modelling assignments in her home town of Yeovil.

CINDY

Yet Cindy, 21, never met the killer Michael Sams, who now begins a life prison sentence in a lonely cell many miles from Cindy's one bedroom flat. And Michael Sams, whose crimes appalled an entire nation, has never heard of her.

BARBIE

But Cindy was never the less brave enough to take off her clothes and pose for nude photographs, in return for £250.

"I read all about Sams in the newspapers", said Cindy, a stunning brunette whose

hobbies include listening to music. "I think it was wrong what he did – killing that woman and that."

LIVING

Cindy hopes to put the memories of Sams evil kidnapping, and of the brutal murder of Julie Dart behind her, and go on to build herself a career as a top model. But it is hard. And the memories are never far away.

CRYING

"He had a wooden leg didn't he? That's right. I remember now. It was in the papers", she said, her frail voice faltering as she slowly put her clothes back on.

Just an ordinary looking trainspotter

There was nothing remarkable about the one legged 51-year-old train spotter standing at the end of the railway platform. As far as station staff or passengers were concerned, he was just another sick-in-the-head trainspotter, obsessed with collecting numbers in little books.

WALKING

But this trainspotter was called Sams. Michael Sams. And he had another hobby – Kidnapping and murder.

SLEEPING

Trainspotting as a hobby has been popular among children – particularly boys – for over a century, and was at its peak during the days of steam.

Each engine is identified by a unique number which it has written on its cab side. The purpose of train spotting is to see as many locomotives as possible. Train spotters carry a special book in which the numbers of all

A typical trainspotter spots a train - and a young boy who is also spotting it, yesterday.

the locomotives are listed, and they use this to tick each one off once it has been spotted. This is called 'copping' a locomotive.

TALKING

Famous train spotters include TV funny man Michael Palin, and former Olympic athlete Tessa Wyatt.

TOMB OF TERROR

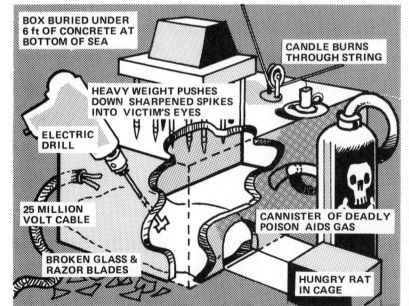

BOX BURIED UNDER 6 ft OF CONCRETE AT BOTTOM OF SEA

CANDLE BURNS THROUGH STRING

HEAVY WEIGHT PUSHES DOWN SHARPENED SPIKES INTO VICTIM'S EYES

ELECTRIC DRILL

25 MILLION VOLT CABLE

BROKEN GLASS & RAZOR BLADES

CANNISTER OF DEADLY POISON AIDS GAS

HUNGRY RAT IN CAGE

THIS IS a sketch of the 'box' in which evil kidnapper Sams held captive his estate agent victim as it was imagined by a graphic artist who has no knowledge whatsoever of the shape, size, dimensions or construction of the actual box used by the killer.

It was in a box absolutely nothing like this that Sam's victim spent quite some time awaiting her eventual release, every second spent in fear of her very life, never knowing whether the box would become her execution chamber, her coffin... or her tomb.

Boxes have been used by criminals for centuries. It was in a box that 'Yorkshire Ripper' mass murderer Peter Sutcliffe kept his packed lunches, prepared for him by his then wife Sonia. And it was in a box that the bloke who lived in Rillington Place, who murdered John Hurt in the film, kept matches which he used to light fires.

Ironically, it was in a box that Sams himself kept tools in his workshop. The same workshop in which is estate agent victim was held captive...in a box. A box which killer Michael Sams has made with those very same tools. Probably.

I SCREWED MY WIFE'S HEAD OFF

-says Sting

Pop star Sting once had sex with his wife so much that her head came off.

Sting – real name Gordon Sting – speaking in an interview with *Women's Things* magazine, told how after having sex for several weeks non-stop, his wife's head flew off.

INFLATABLE SEX

"One night we were doing it for three weeks non stop. When she eventually reached orgasm it was so good her head just seemed to explode – quite literally. It flew through the bedroom window, and landed in my next door neighbour's greenhouse.

VOODOO

I had to go and ask him if I could have her head back. He wasn't very pleased, I can tell you. Her head had broken several panes of

glass and there was smoke coming out of her ears, and she was still smiling for ten months afterwards. That's how good at sex I am".

BLACK MAGIC

But according to the article, the record for stars having sex goes to Hollywood couple Don Johnson and Melanie Griffiths. According to the Miami Vice star, on their honeymoon night the couple had sex an amazing ten million times.

MILK TRAY

A top sex expert we spoke to yesterday confirmed that stars like Sting are better at having sex than ordinary people. "Stars like Sting are better at having sex than ordinary people", he told us yesterday.

20 THINGS YOU NEVER KNEW ABOUT...
BEDS

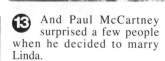

We have sex on them, and breakfast in them. There's reds under them, and mattresses on top of them. Yes, love 'em or hate 'em, there's no getting away from 'em. Beds are here to stay.

So why not lie back with your head on the pillow and enjoy 20 fascinating facts you probably didn't know about beds.

1 Were it not for a print error on the sleeve of their first record, pop group Simply Red would have been called Simply Bed! For singer Mick Hucknall is mad about beds, so much so that as a child he used to lie in every morning.

2 A unique bed – one on which it is claimed Cliff Richard had sex – was sold at Sotherbys in 1981 for a record £31,000.

3 The biggest bed in the world is the Sea Bed, which is so big it doesn't have a mattress. Instead it is covered in soft sand, and is big enough to sleep over a million fish every night.

4 On the subject of sand, Sandy is a town in... you guessed it! *Bed*fordshire.

5 And so is Luton.

6 If you *go to bed* with someone, you don't necessarily share a bed with them for the night. Because *going to bed* with someone is a euphamism adopted by the younger generation, meaning to *have sex*. .

7 So, for example, you could *go to bed* with someone on the sofa, or the kitchen table.

8 Or up against the side of a bus shelter.

9 In the Bible, Joseph and Mary didn't *go to bed*. They conceived the Baby Jesus *immaculately*, which means there was no jiggery pokery involved at all.

10 If you expect a bedsitter to look after your beds for you while you go to the pub, you'll be disappointed. Unlike a babysitter, a bedsitter is a cramped attic room in London containing a filthy mattress and a calor gas stove for which you pay £800 a week rent.

11 You could also be forgiven for thinking a bed pan is a kitchen vessel for the cooking and preparation of beds. But you'd be wrong. A bed pan is in fact a special potty for grown-ups which enables bed-ridden people (people with lots of beds) to go to the toilet without getting up.

12 John Lennon caused a storm of controversy in the sixties when he publicly went to bed with Yoko Ono in an Amsterdam hotel room.

13 And Paul McCartney surprised a few people when he decided to marry Linda.

14 Numerous pop stars have since got themselves into bed conundrums. "All I've got is a s-single bed", sang Noosha Fox in the seventies hit of the same name. Meanwhile, her pop counterpart Gordon Sting of The Police complained "The bed's too big without you".

15 Life is not a bed of roses. However, opinion is divided as to whether it is a minestrone served up with parmesan cheese, a cold lasagne, or a bitch. And then you die.

16 A bed of nails is probably the world's most uncomfortable bed. For it is indeed a blanket of sharp protruding nails slept on by mystical snake charmer types.

17 And it's also the term used to describe any bed belonging to TV's top Geordie pop cop, singer turned actor turned singer again turned writer turned director turned producer, Jimmy Nails.

18 'Ole blue eyes himself, Frank Sinatra, refuses to sleep in the same bed twice. Instead he buys a new bed every day, and has the old one burnt in the morning.

19 A bed bath is not a special water bed which doubles as a bath. It's a popular male fantasy in which Joanne Whalley-Kilner pulls you off whilst dressed in a nurse's uniform.

20 There are two types of bed bug. One is a microscopic insect which lives under your mattress and comes out at night to crawl up your arse. The other is a small listening device which is concealed beneath your bed on your wedding night so that your best man and his mates can listen in to the pathetic sound of you attempting to shag your wife after you've been drinking all day and then dancing all evening with your mother-in-law.

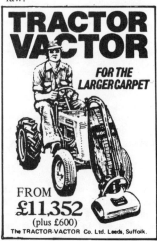

LATER... I KNOW. I'LL TAKE A PHOTOGRAPHIC IMAGE OF YOU ALL! WE COULD PRESENT IT ON OUR RETURN TO GREAT UNCLE SEPTIMUS

HOLD ON, DAD. WHY DON'T YOU USE MY DISC CAMERA?

DISC CAMERA...?

DISC CAMERA! THAT, BOY, IS THE DEVIL'S INSTRUMENT

THERE IS NOTHING WRONG WITH MY "PROFESSOR FOX-TALBOTS PATENT PANOPTICAN PHOTOLITHOGRAPHIC BOX"

RIGHT...STAND STARCHILY AND UNCOMFORTABLY IN A FORMAL GROUP AND ADOPT A MISERABLE EXPRESSION...

...RIGHT... AND PERFECTLY STILL...

TEN MINUTES LATER... ...AND HOLD...

TWENTY MINUTES LATER... ...PERFECTLY STILL...

SUDDENLY... AT-CHOO! SNIFF!

CRIVENS, BOY. DID I NOT TELL YOU TO HOLD THAT POSE PERFECTLY STILL

COME HERE!

WHACK! WHACK! WHACK! WHACK! I'LL HAVE RESPECT FROM YOU BY GOD I WILL!

RIGHT... LET US TRY AGAIN, SHALL WE...?

...AND PERFECTLY STILL...

OH, DEAR!

TWO HOURS LATER... THERE! THE EXPOSURE IS COMPLETE!

NOW!.. LET'S DO ONE FOR GRANDMOTHER

LATER... WIFE! WHERE ARE THE CHILDREN?

I'VE GIVEN THEM A POUND EACH! THEY'VE GONE TO THE AMUSEMENT ARCADES

WHAT!?!

THOSE DENS OF INIQUITY... THOSE... THOSE... TEMPLES TO MAMON! I MUST GO IMMEDIATELY AND SAVE THEM FROM A LIFE OF RUINATION AND VICE

SO... POOL - BINGO - PO AMUSEMENTS AMU

EH? WHAT IS THAT? WHAT THE BUTLER SAW

TSK TSK TSK TSK!! DISGRACEFUL... ...FILTH! WHAT THE BUTLER SAW

...ABSOLUTE FILTH WHAT THE BUTLER SAW

YES! I WAS RIGHT! FILTH! WICKED AND PORNOGRAPHIC DEGRADATION OF THE HUMAN FORM WHAT THE BUTLER SAW

GOD FORGIVE ME, SAVE ME FROM THIS ONANISM... ...OOOH, YEH! BUTLER SAW TUG TUG

TWO HOURS LATER...

EVENTUALLY... DON'T WORRY, MRS. POOTER, HE'S PERFECTLY FINE. HE'S JUST WANKED HIMSELF UNCONSCIOUS WHAT THE BUTLER SAW

90

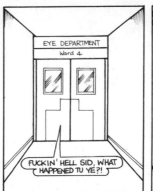

I'VE SEEN THE STA

– and they're not v

It's difficult for us to imagine that stars, just like ordinary people, use the toilet. Somehow we find it hard to believe that TV favourites such as Michael Aspel have wees and poos, and wipe their bottoms with toilet roll.

But like it or not, lavatories are as much a part of TV life as make-up and microphones. And one man who knows that only too well is Frank Crompton who for the last forty-two years has been lavatory attendant at the BBC television centre in London.

Rolls

Over the years, Frank has seen it all. And now, after being sacked in a storm of controversy over missing toilet rolls, he has decided to spill the beans on the stars who use the lavatory, and make public for the first time ever their filthy and disgusting toilet habits.

Baps

"On screen the stars look like a million dollars. But most of it is make-up and clever camera angles. When you see them with their pants round their ankles like I have, their faces screwed up in agony, and you hear the groan of relief as their stools plop into the water, there's nothing glamorous about them, I can tell you.

Jugs

The stars are well known for their extravagant behaviour. They eat well, they drink well, they party a lot, and when they have a turd – boy! Do they have one!

Melons

I'll never forget one log in particular (mainly because it wouldn't flush away, and I had to break its back with a lavatory brush.) Anyway, this one was laid by a particularly well known star. I'll just call her Judith, as I doubt she'd appreciate me giving her full name. But I'll tell you what – there was nothing **Charming** about what she left in my toilet. It had curled itself round the bowl three times, and stank to high heaven. I felt like sending her a postcard saying 'Wish You **Weren't** Here'. The smell was so bad we had to close down the studio next door, and the following day the paint was peeling off the walls and ceiling.

Judith Chalmers

Funnily enough, it's the ladies who are worse than the fellas. What **don't** the birds chuck down the toilet, that's what I want to know. If I'd had a quid for every time I've had to stick my arm round the 'U' bend, in it up to my shoulder, just to pull out a clump of soggy tampons, I'd have a tenner by now. Probably.

Soup

One day the Director General rang me. He said someone had been flushing fag ends down the pan, and they'd caused a blockage somewhere in the pipes. As a result piss was dripping through the roof of the Blue Peter studio.

Garlic bread

That afternoon I saw smoke coming over the top of one of the cubicles, so I grabbed a fire extinguisher and kicked the door in. Surprise, surprise! There was Cilla Black sitting having a crafty cup of tea and a fag. I stopped her just before she threw the fag end down the toilet. "I'll have that", I said to her. It had a bit of a duck's arse on it, but she's a good lass Cilla. She'll always give you a drag on her ciggie.

Cilla - ciggies in the loo

Rippon - 'pebble dashed'

Another bird I recall for less pleasant reasons is Angela Rippon. Boy! Was I glad when she left the Nine O'Clock News. Every time I saw her coming I'd say "And now for the Nine O'Clock Poos!" You see, she was terrible with the nerves, and every evening at about five to nine she's come busting down the corridor, farting like a tractor.

Steak sandwich

It would be ungentlemanly of me to go into any further detail. Suffice to say that when she'd finished it looked like someone had been in and pebble-dashed half the bloody cubicle. By, it took some getting off, that did. In the end I had to get a hosepipe and jet the whole place out with water.

Erm...

There was one or two well behaved stars who'd leave the place as they found it. The magician Ali Bongo was one, but how he did it I'll never know.

Dump

One day he popped in for a quick dump during rehearsels for his show. I know it was him 'cos I looked under the cubicle door and recognised his curly slippers. Anyway, he must have had a massive turd, cos I heard the sound it made when it hit the water. My first thought was 'I hope the flush shifts that bastard – 'cos I don't fancy doing it with a brush'.

Next thing I knew he got up and left, no wiping, no flushing – no sound at all. I thought 'Here we go – another mess for Yours Truly to clean up'. But when I got into the cubicle, I couldn't believe my eyes. It was as clean as a whistle. Nothing in the pan, and no mess at all.

Tip

This happened several times. Every time he'd lay a log, then leave without flushing it. But there was never anything in the toilet.

VIZ No.1 FOR STORIES ABOUT THE STARS' COCKS

So the next time he came in I peeped over the top of the next cubicle to see what was going on.

Insult

What I saw was the most amazing thing I've ever seen happen in a toilet – and I've seen a few, I can tell you! There was Ali Bongo standing sprinkling his magic woofle dust over an enormous glistening log that was so big it was practically climbing out of the pan. Then suddenly POOF! It disappeared in a puff of smoke. To this day, I've never worked out how he did it.

Hygiene is very important, specially when you work in a lavatory. So I would wash my hands every day when I got home from work. But some of the stars didn't seem so bothered.

Summon

I remember one occasion we ran out of loo roll. It was coming up to lunch time and I knew a lot of stars would probably fancy a shit during their dinner break. So I popped out to the shop to get some paper.

When I got back I was surprised to see a well known academic quiz show host who shall remain nameless, leaving the cubicle. What he'd wiped his bottom with I'll never know. But put it this way – his tie was looking a bit dishevelled to say the least!

Hail

Anyway, he then proceeded to walk straight out without washing his hands. Five minutes later I saw him tucking into a '*starter for ten*' in the BBC canteen – with his fingers.

...ARS' COCKS
...y big, I can tell you

Some big-hearted stars made working in a lavatory fun, and I'd always look forward to visits from cheery multi-talented big C all clear tap dancing trumpet player Roy Castle. Music's in his blood, and he'd always sing while he had a dump after filming 'Record Breakers'.

Roy - Big heart

Little and Large (above) - Large (below) and Little (above). Jimmy Nail (below) - Large nose, little cock. And (inset, above, below, right) Little and Large's Large pulls a face.

"Defecation. Defecation. Defecation – that's what you need." Those were the words he'd use. And he'd always play a little tune on his trumpet too. At least I *think* it was his trumpet!

One day they popped in for a piss during a break from recording their great comedy show. And when I looked over their shoulders, I got quite a surprise. I'll tell you what – the names are right – 'Little and Large'. But with no disrespect to Eddie Large, I think someone got them the wrong way round!

On one occasion Roy must have produced a 'Record Breaker' himself. He dashed out of the cubicle, and told me not to flush it. Then he came rushing back with Noris McWhirter and a tape measure.

Rolling

That might have been a big one, but I think the record goes to Stewart Hall from 'It's A Knockout'. One day he produced a specimen which *was* a knockout – quite literally. One whiff of it and I was gone! When I eventually regained consciousness we called in his old pal Arthur Ellis with his Halifax Brewery dipstick to measure the water displacement.

Gall

While number twos are always the most exciting, it's the everyday number ones which are a toilet attendant's bread and butter. Mopping up the piss was a never ending task. Of course, as I cleaned the floor I couldn't help but get a glimpse of the stars' cocks. And just like the stars themselves, their cocks come in all shapes and sizes. A fine example being Little and Large.

Cheek

Thursday evenings were always busy, 'cos I'd get the Top Of The Pops crowd in. Come to think of it, I must be the envy of every bird in Britain. 'Cos there's not one pop star's cock I haven't seen. Mind, some of 'em you have to try pretty hard to see at all. Like 'Microscopic' Mick Hucknall out of Simply Red. Don't worry girls – you aren't missing much there, I can tell you.

Hole

Jimmy Nail is another one who doesn't live up to expectations. I don't think 'Nail' was a particularly good choice of surname. 'Half-Inch Panel Pin' would have been more appropriate, from what I saw.

Of course, it's not only the stars who have tiny tackles. A lot of the high ups at the BBC – like the Director General – are short of a few inches in that department. And I suspect that jealousy may have been partly to blame for my recent dismissal. They said it was because I'd stolen some toilet rolls – but I'd only borrowed them. I was planning to bring them back the following day.

Rap

I think the real reason is my dead big cock. Frankly, I don't think the egotistical stars or the snobby bosses at the BBC could handle someone working in the toilet with a much bigger cock than them. **99**

Edmonds caught in 'Moon monkey' sting

A host of gullible TV celebrities – among them House Party star Noel Edmonds – have lost money to a cheeky con man wearing a false beard and claiming to be the Prince of Wales.

The trickster, who is wanted by police for fraud, approached several wealthy showbusiness stars in 1992, and told them he was raising funds to send a rocket to the moon. He smooth talked them into believing that Russian experimental space monkeys, launched into orbit during the sixties, were now trapped on the Moon, and £10 million was needed to build a rocket to take them bananas.

TV Noel yesterday - Moon monkey mercy mission

MONKEYS

Noel was touched by the apparent plight of the monkeys, and from the Crinkley bottom of his heart he handed over several million pounds towards the moon mercy mission. Indeed, he even offered to drive the space rocket which was due to take off next year. But shortly after being handed £5 million for 'rocket parts', the mystery man disappeared, leaving Noel and a host of other stars, including David Bowie, out of pocket.

BEATLES

The police yesterday issued a warning to all stars, telling them to beware of anyone claiming to be the Prince of Wales, and to exercise caution whenever dealing with unusual requests for large sums of cash.

Edmonds is by no means the first star to be easily parted from his money. In 1988 pop star Sting – real name Mr G. Sting – handed over a box containing £12 million cash to a man with a false moustache who claimed that Martian rain forests were being cut down by aliens from another galaxy. Mr Sting was told that the cash was needed to launch a campaign to save the Martian space trees, and bring a Martian back to Earth to go on chat shows.

POLOS

But after being given the money the man jumped into his car and drove off.

Yes, we have no bananas - a monkey similar to those 'trapped on the moon'.

U2 JOKE

CAREFUL DEAR. DON'T GO TOO NEAR THE EDGE.

ROGER MELLIE

THE MAN ON THE TELLY WHO SAYS **BOLLOCKS!**

ROGER HAS BEEN CALLED IN TO TOM'S OFFICE...

YOU WANTED TO SEE ME TOM

YES ROGER. TAKE A LOOK AT THIS

LLOYD WEBER'S THOMAS THE TANK ENGINE SHOW HITS TECHNICAL SNAG

TURN TABLE IS TO BLAME

PAGE THREE IS IT? SEEN IT ALREADY, TOM. SMASHING PAIR OF JUGS ON HER!

NO ROGER. THIS IS 'VARIETY', THE SHOWBIZ PAPER

MUSICAL STARTS CASTING

THERE'S A JOB VACANCY I THINK YOU OUGHT TO LOOK AT

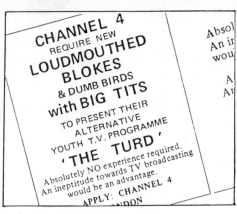

THE TURD, EH? THAT'S A KIDS SHOW ISN'T IT?

YES, IT IS. BUT I'VE GOT A FEELING THAT IT WOULD BE RIGHT UP YOUR STREET

HANDS UP IF YOU THINK KENNETH BRANNAN'S A TWAT

CHARLIE DRAKE IN THE COMEBACK TRAIL

Variety

WOMBLES MUSICAL STARTS CASTING

Wombles Back

IT'S A HAPPENING, LATE NIGHT, YOUTH ORIENTATED, ZOO FORMAT SHOW, ROGER. AND THEY HAVE A HISTORY OF, ERM.... LET'S SAY **CONTROVERSIAL** PRESENTERS

MMM... I WONDER WHAT THE MONEY'S LIKE

I'LL RING CHANNEL 4 TODAY AND SEE IF I CAN FIX UP AN AUDITION

THE NEXT DAY....

CHANNEL 4

OH DEAR. I WONDER WHERE ROGER IS. I HOPE HE'S NOT GOING TO BE LATE FOR THE AUDITION

AH, TOM. **HI!** IS ROGER HERE YET? ONLY WE'RE ON A BIT OF TIGHT SCHEDULE TODAY

HE SHOULD BE HERE ANY MINUTE.

IT'S NOT LIKE HIM TO BE LATE

CAN I BE FRANK WITH YOU TOM? WE'RE A BIT WORRIED THAT ROGER IS TOO, ERM... **OLD** FOR A **YOUTH** SHOW LIKE THE **TURD**. WE REALLY WANT SOMEONE THE KIDS CAN **RELATE** TO

I THINK YOU'LL BE SURPRISED WHEN YOU MEET ROGER. I'M SURE YOU'LL LIKE HIM. GIVE HIM A CHANCE, EH? SEE WHAT HE'S GOT TO SAY.

FUCK ME TOM! GUESS WHO I JUST WALKED PAST IN THE CORRIDOR? MY FAVOURITE WANK; THAT'S ALL! **MARIETTA** BLEEDIN' **FOSTRUPP!!** THE SEXY BLONDE BIRD OFF THE TELLY

THAT'S WHY I'M LATE ACTUALLY. COULDN'T RESIST NIPPING INTO THE GENTS FOR A QUICK **TOLL** ON THE OLD **BELL** END!

ROGER, WHEN CAN YOU START?

TWO WEEKS LATER AT THE TURD'S STUDIOS...

TOM, I'M **EXCITED**!! OUR NEW PRESENTERS ARE GOING TO BE A **BIG HIT** WITH **THE KIDS**. ROGER IS TOTALLY **OUTRAGEOUS**, AND OUR NEW GIRL HAS GOT REALLY **BIG TITS**

WHERE **IS** ROGER?

WE JUST SENT HIM DOWN TO WARDROBE FOR SOME BIG, DAFT, BAGGY, ITALIAN CLOTHES

ROGER! YOU LOOK **SO SEXY!**

THAT'S ODD. I FEEL LIKE A RIGHT CUNT.

COME ON. LET ME INTRODUCE YOU TO EVERYONE

ATTENTION EVERYONE! THIS IS ROGER, OUR NEW PRESENTER

NICE T'MEET YER ORLRAAAAHT?

HI ROGER. FAB! TEE HEE! GIGGLE!

ROGER, THESE ARE YOUR CO-PRESENTERS. THIS IS TERRY, WHO HAS AN UGLY FACE AND STRONG PROVINCIAL ACCENT, AND THAT IS THE GIRL WITH THE BIG TITS

NOW THEN, THE SHOW GOES OUT LIVE, AND STARTS IN TEN MINUTES. I'LL RUN THROUGH THE GUESTS FOR YOU IF YOU LIKE

OVER THERE ARE FOUR EXCEEDINGLY SMUG AND PRETENTIOUS BASTARDS FROM MANCHESTER CALLED **THIRD REICH**. THEY WERE CALLED **FUN FACTORY** TILL THEIR LEAD SINGER TOPPED HIMSELF. THEY'VE NEVER LOOKED BACK SINCE.

TERRY IS GOING TO ACCUSE THEM OF BEING NAZIS LATER TO TRY AND GET SOME SORT OF ROW GOING.

THEN THE GIRL WITH **BIG TITS** WILL BE DOING A LIVE SATELLITE INTERVIEW WITH **M.C. SCREWDRIVER** ABOUT HIS RAP RECORD "COP KILLING QUEER CASTRATER"

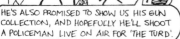

HE'S ALSO PROMISED TO SHOW US HIS GUN COLLECTION, AND HOPEFULLY HE'LL SHOOT A POLICEMAN LIVE ON AIR FOR 'THE TURD'.

WE ALSO HAVE BADLY BEHAVED BRITISH ACTOR **OLIVER REID-PIPE** ON THE SHOW. WE'VE HIDDEN A CAMERA IN HIS DRESSING ROOM

WE'VE GIVEN HIM FREE BEER ALL AFTERNOON, AND NAILED HIS TOILET DOOR SHUT. HOPEFULLY HE'LL STAGGER ABOUT A BIT, SAY SOMETHING RUDE, THEN WET HIMSELF.

AND THIS IS **TOTALLY** BRILLIANT! WE'LL KEEP GOING BACK TO THIS FEATURE THROUGHOUT THE SHOW. OVER HERE WE'VE GOT THREE DRUNKEN BUTCHERS APPRENTICES

COCK CHOP CHALLENGE

PETE · MICK · JOHN

THEY'RE GOING TO CUT THEIR OWN COCKS OFF AND MAKE THEM INTO SAUSAGES, AND THE GUESTS WILL HAVE TO EAT THEM AT THE END OF THE SHOW!

OKAY ROGER, WE'RE ON THE AIR IN TEN SECONDS...

ERM...

JUST ONE THING. DO I HAVE A SCRIPT AT ALL?

SCRIPT? OF COURSE NOT. JUST REMEMBER – KEEP QUESTIONS TRIVIAL, AND DON'T WORRY ABOUT WHICH CAMERA TO LOOK AT.

AS LONG AS IT ISN'T THE ONE THAT'S ON

OKAY... STAND BY EVERYONE... 3-2-1...

AT LAST, ROGER'S FOUND HIS TRUE VOCATION!

AND NOW ON CHANNEL 4 IT'S TIME FOR MUSIC, CONTROVERSY, SEXISM AND SWEARING AS WE BEGIN A NEW SERIES OF... **THE TURD**...

PRESENTED BY ROGER MELLIE, TERRY ATHEIST AND A DAFT GIRL WITH BIG TITS

HI KIDS! WELCOME TO THE SHOW. WE'VE GOT A WONDERFUL EVENING'S ENTERTAINMENT LINED UP FOR YOU TONIGHT. SOMETHING FOR EVERYONE!

I'M YOUR NEW HOST ROGER MELLIE, AND I HOPE YOU ENJOY THE SHOW AS MUCH AS I WILL ENJOY PRESENTING IT.

WHAT'S GOING ON?

ERM... HE JUST NEEDS TO WARM UP, THAT'S ALL

FIRST, LET'S KICK OFF THE PARTY WITH A SUPER BAND WHO I KNOW WE'RE ALL LOOKING FORWARD TO SEEING

COME ON KIDS. LET'S HEAR IT! LET'S HAVE A BIG WARM WELCOME FOR THE ONE AND ONLY **THIRD REICH**!

SO FAR SO GOOD, EH?

ROGER. ARE YOU ALRIGHT?

ROGER! CAN I HAVE A QUICK WORD WITH YOU PLEASE

I THINK THAT WAS A TINY BIT TOO... ERM... **STIFF**. LOOSEN UP A BIT, EH? REMEMBER, THIS IS **YOUTH** T.V.

DON'T BE AFRAID TO SHOOT FROM THE HIP. SAIL A BIT CLOSER TO THE WIND, YOU KNOW. LET YOUR HAIR DOWN. SPEAK YOUR MIND A LITTLE.

AAH! I'M WITH YOU. YOU WANT SOMETHING **NEAR THE KNUCKLE**. A BIT **RISQUE** YOU MEAN.

EXACTLY!

NO PROBLEM. LEAVE IT TO ME. I'M A PRO. LET'S **GO FOR IT!**

THAT'S THIRD REICH THERE, WITH THEIR NEW SINGLE 'BLUE SUNDAY'. AND, ER...

FLIPPING HECK KIDS! WERE THOSE GUYS **GREAT** OR **WHAT**?!

TERRY WILL BE CHATTING TO THEM LATER. BUT NOW ITS OVER TO OUR COCK CHOPPING CHALLENGE...

FACKING HELL TOM, THIS GUY IS A **TOTAL** SQUARE! NO SMUTTY INNUENDO, NO VULGARITY. NO ILL CONCEIVED REMARKS. NOTHING!

I CAN'T UNDERSTAND IT. ROGER HAS NEVER BEHAVED LIKE THIS BEFORE

AFTER THE SHOW...

NOT A BAD SHOW, EH? THAT OLIVER REID-PIPE WAS A BIT PISSED, BUT I MANAGED TO SHUT HIM UP BEFORE HE SAID ANYTHING SILLY.

NOT A BAD SHOW!!?? IT WAS A **DISASTER!**

WE'LL BE LUCKY IF WE GET A SINGLE COMPLAINT!

HERE'S THE VIEWING FIGURES, FABIEN. THERE WAS **EIGHTEEN** PEOPLE WATCHING THE SHOW, BUT THREE OF THEM WERE ASLEEP.

EIGHTEEN EH?

IT WAS **THAT** BAD WAS IT?

EIGHTEEN! THAT'S NOT BAD AT ALL! IT'S SIX UP ON THE AVERAGE FOR OUR LAST SERIES!

WELL, FUCK ME SIDEWAYS! THIS CALLS FOR A CELEBRATION.

FIRST A BIT OF **SERIOUS** DRUG ABUSE, FOLLOWED BY A FRENZIED **GROUP SEX ORGY** WITH A FEW OF THOSE DIRTY LOOKING BIRDS IN THE AUDIENCE!

ROGER, DARLING...

WHY COULDN'T YOU HAVE SAID THAT WHEN WE WERE ON THE AIR?

CD. ST 9 93

LetterBocks

Wrong address

I am writing to you to enquire about placing an advertisement in your magazine. I wish to start in the mail order business and would appreciate any advice you could give me. The product I wish to seel are Laser Specs which when worn give a psychedelic coloured starburst effect.

R. Grice
Telford

Unfortunately the address you have written to is our Letterbocks address Mr Grice. The correct address to write to would be our ad. sales department at John Brown Publishing, The Boathouse, Crabtree Lane, Fulham, London SW6.

Take British Telecom's latest high tech fibre optic digitalised network, combine this with Nat West's latest worldwide computerised banking and sorting system, add one second class stamp and what have you got? A bank statement nine fucking days out of date.

P. S. Doff
Leeds

Hair's a thing

Whenever I see pubic hairs stuck to my soap bar I smile. We normal folk should be thankful that we have so much hair to spare. Just think of all the poor bald people whose heads will be getting cold this winter.

C. Litter
Ryhope

LETTERBOCKS
Viz, P.O.Box 1PT
Newcastle upon Tyne
NE99 1PT

For the benefit of Mr Lomax of Sudbury, (Letterbocks, Viz 61), the actor Jeff Goldblum drinks piss during TV lager commercials because he gets paid a million pounds by the Germans to do so. If someone paid me half that amount I'd happily lick the clinkers off their underpants.

M. Richards
(No relation)

Hearing voices

Whose idea of a sick joke was it to start giving voices to electrical apparatus? Only the other day my iron informed me that it needed more distilled water, the toaster told me it was full of crumbs, and my bedside table lamp told me to go out and kill women.

R. Hutch
Yorkshire

I'd like to get my hands on the pop star who recorded the song 'White Lines Don't Do It'. My son decided to take his advice, and ended up getting the sack from his job . He worked for the council painting white lines in the middle of the road.

Mr D. Kennel
Hull

In issue 61 of your magazine, page 23, fifth column, you show British Railways locomotive number 86001 and the caption reads '...a train... yesterday' well for your information British Railways policy is to renumber locomotives when alterations or modifications are carried out and I'm afraid that your picture was not taken 'yesterday' because locomotive number 86001 was renumbered number 86401 in 1987, actually.

R. Smith
Byker, Newcastle

Well spotted Mr Smith. You win first prize in our Pedantic Small Minded Trainspotter Competition. A copy of Razzle is on its way to you.

Dyslexic? Bone idle more like it.

Victor Ian Values
London N4

One for the road

I don't know what all the fuss is about drink driving. I *drink drive* every day. I'm a drayman for the local brewery, and *drive drink* to dozens of pubs every week.

B. McCannel
Portstewart

P.S. Come to think of it I do drink quite a lot of it as well.

With all these foreign football clubs naming themselves after electricity, such as AC Milan and Dynamo Tbleisi, isn't it about time English clubs followed suit? I for one would be proud to support Manchester Capacitors, Aston Fusewire or Wolverhampton Integrated Circuit Breakers.

The Manager, Tandy
Cheshunt, Herts

A friend of mine (God) mentioned that it might not be too late to enter your laughing Policemen competition. Here's a few pictures I had taken at short notice. Any good?

J. Anderton
Manchester

Bank on a Viz sell out

Ten years ago Viz carried a spoof advertisement for the 'GnatWest' bank. In the last issue there was a whole page advertisement for 'Barclays'. But it was serious. Talk about a sell out. What next? Student Grant appearing in a national bank advertising campaign?

Mark Ruston
Manchester

No Mark. Smirnoff vodka. But we'd be very keen to hear from any bank's who were interested in securing Student Grant's services in the future.

You talk crap, sap

For Spr. Collier's information (Letterbocks, Viz 61) troops in Bosnia don't get free phone calls home, they pay for their stamps, and Sam Fox is just an old slapper who didn't even get her tits our and only turned up to get her picture in the paper. Meanwhile, you and your mates in Belize enjoy a tropical holiday drinking rum, smoking pot, shagging prostitutes and getting a sun tan.

Pte's S. Pinchess
and W. Taylor

Sapper Collier certainly stirred up a hornet's nest of controversy with his remarks, provoking a sackful of letters from squaddies all over the world. We couldn't possibly print all of them, but some of the best names he was called were 'whingeing fuckwit', 'puff', 'Spr. Cholera', 'sap' and 'sciving twat'.

Next week: 'Loads-of-Money' has his car serviced and the bill comes to £186.00

s of wank on

Having read Mr Values' letter (this issue) on the subject of dyslexia, I bet you £50 you get a letter of complaint from the National Dyslexia Association within ten days of its publication.

A. Punter
West Bromwich

It's a bet, on the condition that whoever wins gives the money to them.

Further to my previous letter on this page. Right. You're on.

A. Punter
West Bromwich

Will you please help me settle an argument between myself and a friend. My friend says Viz has always been crap, wheras I say it used to be quite funny. Which of us is right?

N. Y. Ross
Ross-on-Wye

TOE NAIL clippings, chopped up finely, make an ideal substitute for wood chippings when repairing wood chip wallpaper.

T. Marriage
Fulham

WHY PAY for expensive jigsaws? Just take a bag of frozen chips from the freezer and try piecing together potatoes.

B. Reastford
Ironville, Notts.

FELLAS. Play 'Rodeo Sex' by shagging your missus 'doggy fashion' and then calling her another bird's name. See how long you can stay on for!

Karin Love
Nottingham

FAT PEOPLE. Pay someone to walk along behind you juggling, swallowing swords or eating fire etc. to divert attention from your obesity.

R. Warren
Teddington

ANOREXICS. When your knees become fatter than your legs start eating cakes again.

P. Loft
Gateshead

TOP TiPS

MAKE neighbours think you have Norwegian visitors staying by leaving old whalebones outside the back door along with your rubbish.

E.M.
North Shields

ALWAYS carry a five pence piece in your pocket so that if you fancy a chinese takeaway you can buy a fork.

H. Attwell
Enfield

WHEN photographing windmills attach a white handkerchief to the end of one of the sails. When the pictures are developed this will be invaluable in indicating both wind direction and sail rotation.

R. Well
Holland

AVOID parking tickets by leaving your windscreen wipers turned on to 'fast wipe' whenever you leave your car parked illegally.

S. Tyler
Norwich

DON'T waste electricity flashing your headlights to allow buses to pull out in front of you. They invariably do so anyway.

H. Attwell
Enfield

MAKE motorists slow down in your street by getting your wife to dress as a police woman and point a hair drier at them as they pass by.

R. Nest
Chippenham

A. PELLING. Avoid having hoards of angry 'townies' descend on your house by sending us £10 cash. If you don't we'll publish your full address in the next issue.

The Editors
Viz Magazine

REVIVE dying moths by placing them on a small droplet of sugary water.

C. Coup
Basildon

MAKE sex with your wife more exciting by telling her to wear lots of lipstick and wash her mouth out with vodka. Then you can pretend you're shagging some old scrubber you've just picked up in a nightclub.

F. Lair
Kelso

GOING THROUGH THE MOTIONS

By our Science Correspondent **Lulu**

Nobody likes to dwell on their droppings. We tend to flush our faeces down the toilet the minute we've finished wiping our bottoms. But according to one new theory, we could be making a big mistake.

An increasing number of doctors now believe that faecal examination – that's looking at your poo to you and me – is an excellent way to monitor your health. For the colour, content, texture and smell of a number two reveals vital information about the lifestyle that you lead.

TURD

"Every turd is a little mine of information", says Dr. Emilo Budweiser, Head of Excrement at Los Angeles University's Institute of Advanced Toilet Research.

STOOL

"Every stool is like a book just waiting to be read. Every

dollop a brand new chapter, packed with information. And winnits are like micro film, jam packed with valuable data about the human body", he continued.

MUSHITROOM

In his new book 'Learning From Our Stools', Dr. Budweiser recommends that we all take time to scrutinise our droppings for a few moments each day, probing it with a fork, or an old tooth brush. By doing so all manner of information can be discerned. Here's a few clues to look out for, together with the information that they reveal.

Do you recognise any of the following poo properties?

PEANUTS – If you find traces of peanut amongst your stool, you may well be a party person – someone who likes a nibble in the pub perhaps, or alternatively someone who enjoys crunchy peanut butter.

SWEETCORN – This suggests a healthy lifestyle. You enjoy vegetables – sweetcorn in particular. You might also enjoy corn on the cob. Sweetcorn is generally a healthy sign.

SLOPPY STOOLS – If you suffer from runny poo this is an indication of bad diet, and of possible stomach problems. You may lead a stressful life, suffer from anxiety, or perhaps you just had a big curry last night.

DARK "FUDGY" STOOLS – This could be a sign that you drink Guinness.

FAT WITH A HAT

Send us the name of a fat person and the type of hat you'd like to see them wearing. We pay £5 for every suggestion we use.

This week: Actor Stratford Johns wears a trilby hat, as suggested by Kate Remmington, 32, of Macclesfield. Congratulations Kate, there's a crisp fiver on its way to you.

99

'BOARD' BONEO GOES CHESS NUTS

Pop idol Boneo, lead singer with Irish rockers U2, has swapped his guitar for a chess set. And instead of playing hits like 'Sunday Bloody Sunday', the millionaire musician is playing chess – 24 hours a day.

Bored with the rock and roll lifestyle, Boneo, who has several 'O' levels, decided to exercise his intellect by taking up the high brow game last year. And already he has impressed friends and colleagues with his chess playing ability, beating The Edge three times in a row and becoming a Grand Master at the game.

GOAL

And Boneo's new found ambition is to achieve the ultimate goal in chess and become World Champion by beating the world's top players like Nigel Short and Boris Karloff.

TRY

Boneo is by no means the only star who has taken to treading the board game boards. Many celebrities have achieved world class status playing board games. With only one show a week many TV stars find themselves with lots of spare time, time which they often put to good use achieving world class status in the world of board games.

BASKET

And for a skillful player the rewards can be great, for there are handsome cash prizes to be won, earning top telly stars vital extra income. For example in 1982, magician Paul Daniels picked up a cool £180,000 when he became World Champion 'Kerplunk!' player. At the

By our Chess, Party Games & Table Tennis Correspondent **YVONNE GOOLAGONG**

U2 star swaps pop for prawns

time 'not a lot' star Paul Daniels was earning only £50 a week for his BBC show.

RUN

Other big money game winners include Bruce Springsteen (United States 'W.H. Smith Magnetic Fishing' Champion 1979), Ludovik Kennedy (undefeated British 'Twister' champion 1981-1993) and Bamber Gasgoine who won the coveted European Triple Crown back in 1977 when he collected first prizes in 'Mousetrap', 'Buckaroo' and 'My Cat's Got Flees' at

the triathlon event at the Birmingham NEC in front of a spellbound audience of 18,000 game fanatics.

WICKET

Big game winners like Gasgoine can earn anything up to £700,000 a year from exhibition games alone, playing in packed venues all around the world. There is also big money to be made in sponsorship deals, as well as the usual perks which include free nail scissors, soap, and sizeable discounts on garden furniture.

CZECH MATES - Boneo can count among his friends U2's many fans in the former Czechoslovakia. If he wants.

PLAY CHESS WITH BONEO

Chess is often viewed as a minority interest sport, and many youngsters find the game boring and confusing to play. But nothing could be further from the truth, according to U2's Boneo. So we asked him to tell us a little about the game and how it is played in the hope that more people will take up the game and derive pleasure from it.

'Chess isn't like football or cricket. There's no ball, and you don't have to run around. You play it indoors, and so it doesn't matter if it's raining.

PLAYERS

There are two players, blacks versus whites. I always like to be blacks, cos one of my white prawns is missing and I have to use a button instead. But it's got 'prawn' written on it to avoid any confusion. The prawns go along the front, and the rest go along the back. It tells you the positions on the box usually.

You always start by moving a prawn. They go

two squares forward first, then one. Or across ways if they're overtaking someone. The horses are my favourite. They go three forwards and two sideways, or the other way round. That's the hardest one to remember, but I remember it by thinking that it's like two sides of a shoebox, kind of thing.

BENSONS

Castles are dead easy. They just go forwards. I think they can reverse, and they might be able to go sideways, but I'm not sure. But definitely not across. Bishops go slanty ways. And the King and Queen can go anywhere they want. But if someone overtakes your King they check mate you.

CRAVEN 'A'

It's best to remember that chess is just like a race. You have to overtake their bits before they overtake you. If you land on someone, you've overtaken them, and they go back in the box. And when someone's got no bits left, that means they've lost.

£ £ £ £ £ £ £ £ £ £ £ £ £ £

Game stars who dress like a million pounds

Lucrative sponsorship deals earn millions of pounds for successful game players. Here's how a TV star can earn a fortune moonlighting at Monopoly, or playing Sorry on the side.

WOODBINES

Top agents will ensure that every item of a stars clothing is sponsored. And this is how the millions add up.

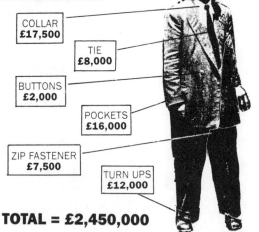

COLLAR £17,500

TIE £8,000

BUTTONS £2,000

POCKETS £16,000

ZIP FASTENER £7,500

TURN UPS £12,000

TOTAL = £2,450,000

EXCUSE ME SIR, BUT YOUR FATHER HAS JUST DIED.

THIS ONE'S FOR PA

golf joke

the end

100

SAVE THIS POOR COW

Barbaric French villagers plan to MURDER this tragic defenceless cow, HACK its lifeless carcass into bloody pieces, COOK it in an oven, then EAT it.

BY OUR EUROPHOBE CORRESPONDENT BILLY BOLLOCKS

And then the blood thirsty mob will wash down its remains with bottles of wine.

BARBARIC

This barbaric ritual, reminiscent of a scene from the middle ages, has been re-enacted in the streets of Purtain sur le Lit every year for centuries. This year it will be no different, and the French authorities have no intention of lifting a finger to stop it.

PEASANTS

Paraded out of its field by stick wielding peasants, the terrified beast will then be herded into a waiting lorry like cattle before being driven a short distance along bumpy roads to the local abattoir.

PETRIFIED

As a throng of jeering abattoir employees look on, the petrified animal will be **STUNNED** with electricity, and then **KILLED** with a savage blow to the head from a bolt.

CUE

That will be the cue for cheering crowds of sadistic

HOLSTEIN-FRIESIAN

French shoppers to go on the rampage through the narrow streets of the town, queuing in the butchers shop and supermarkets to buy blood stained chunks of the pathetic animal's body, which only hours before had been standing harmlessly in a field.

REST

Local civic dignitaries, among them the town's Mayor, will all join in the shameful procession as the animals corpse is carried bit by bit back to kitchens to be cooked and later eaten, together with potatoes and vegetables.

"If this is what passes for civilisation on the continent then we have to ask ourselves whether we, the British, really want to be a part of it", said Tory MP Sir Anthony Regents-Park yesterday. "I don't deny that animals must sometimes be killed out of necessity. But the least they could do would be to give the poor beasts a chance by perhaps chasing them around on horseback with a pack of baying hounds, or charging a wealthy Arab £5,000 a day to drive around in a Range Rover taking pot shots at them with a shotgun. To subject an animal to such an undignified ritual seems quite wrong in this modern age".

Help bring a French cow back to Britain

We want to send a message loud and clear to the townsfolk of Purtain sur le Lit: "FROG OFF!". And we need your help.

We're launching a campaign to save a cow from the hands of the French butchers, and gathering signatures for a vital petition aimed at stopping the slaughter. We want you to get five people to sign the form below, and send it back to us together with a donation of £5 (cash only).

SPIDER

The forms will be collected, and then sent to the Mayor of Purtain sur le Lit, telling him in no uncertain terms where he can shove his onions, cheap plonk and silly loafs of bread.

The cash raised will be used to buy a French cow, transport it to England, and put it in a field with lots of grass. And some trees. It may be too late for the sad cow in our picture, but together we can save another cow. So send in the form, and money, today. The address is SAVE A FRENCH COW, Viz, P.O. Box 1PT, Newcastle upon Tyne, NE99 1PT.

For extra petition forms send £2.50 to the same address.

To: The Mayor, Purtain-sur-le-Lit, France

Dear Mayor,
FROG OFF! You MURDERER!
Signed 1 _____
2 _____ 3 _____
4 _____ 5 _____

IT'S GAZ TOP MANIA!

Britain's pop fans have gone Gaz Top potty!

He's the TV presenter who's *Gaz* top of everyone's *Gaz* pops! With his cute little lisp and blacker than black lavatory brush hairdo, he's the *Gaz* top of the pop top pop presenter who the girls are *Gaz*pin' to meet.

TOAST

Yes, he's Gaz Top. The pop host with the *Gaz Top* most! He's the toast of Britain's TV pops. The Pop Tart who's top of every chart! "Top – top – top, popability! That's the beauty of Gaz!"

CELEBRATE

To celebrate Britain's top pop presenter, and because we've got nothing better to write about, we're giving away a host of *Gaz* top prizes! And as Gaz would doubtless agree, it's a

WIN £100 IN RECORD VOUCHERS

Gaztoptastic array of goodies that are up for grabs!

ENTER

All you have to do to enter our *Gaztopcompetition* is *Gaz* answer two easy peasy questions and send us a drawing of the man himself. We'll be asking Gaz Top himself to *Gaz* choose the *Gaz* top entry, and our first prize of £100's worth of *Gaz* top *Gaz* pop record vouchers will be sent to the

Gaz lucky winner. Answer these simple *Gaz Top* questions:

1. Which TV programme, if any, is Gaz Top currently presenting?

2. Arrange these 3 star qualities which Gaz possesses into order of importance, No. 1 for the most important, and 3 for the least: Village idiot charm, imbecilic good looks, all round Gaz Top popability.

Send your entries to Viz Top of the Gaz Pops Competition, P.O. Box 1PT, Newcastle upon Tyne, NE99 1PT. If Gaz Top is reading this and would like to judge our competition, could he please get in touch. If he wants to give us a ring we will accept a reverse charge call.

HACKLES' MOISTS present
MORE TALES OF THE EVER-HIDEOUS...

BOTTOM INSPECTORS

A SATURDAY AFTERNOON... A BUSY SHOPPING STREET...

SHALL WE STOP FOR A CUP OF TEA SOON?

YES.

OOH. LOOK AT THIS BARBRA.

NOTICE

THE OFFICE OF BOTTOM INSPECTION HEREBY ANNOUNCE A

BOTTOM AMNESTY

TO ANY PERSON CHECKING IN AT THIS MOBILE UNIT FOR A FREE BOTTOM INSPECTION TODAY. NO PUNISHMENT - GUARANTEED. COUNSELLING AVAILABLE.

YES. YOU DO WORRY A LOT ABOUT BEING INSPECTED, THIS SEEMS VERY INTERESTING.

IT SEEMS LIKE A NEW IDEA FROM THE BOTTOM INSPECTORS. I HOPE IT'S A GENUINE OFFER.

...IT'S A WHOLE NEW ATTITUDE... MY FRIENDS.

GASP!

CHOKE!

HEH! HEH! HEH!..

YOU SEE, WE'VE LEARNED A FEW LITTLE LESSONS FROM OUR FRIENDS IN SOCIAL SERVICES. YOU SEE NOT ALL BOTTOM CRIMINALS MEAN HARM...

...IT IS OFTEN THE CASE THAT THEY HAVE SIMPLY LEARNED BAD HABITS THROUGH A CHILDHOOD OF BOTTOM NEGLECT.

SUCH PEOPLE NEED NO PUNISHMENT, THEY NEED TO BE UNDERSTOOD, THEY NEED A SECOND CHANCE. PLEASE STEP INSIDE.

OH. WHAT A NICE MAN.

THANKYOU. MOST KIND.

INSIDE... IF YOU JUST STEP INTO ONE BOOTH EACH, POP YOUR THINGS OFF, AND SOMEONE WILL BE WITH YOU SHORTLY.

MEANWHILE... THANKS FOR COMING. KEEP THOSE CLEFTS SQUEAKY CLEAN NOW WON'T YOU. ...BYE BYE.

CERTAINLY, WHAT A GREAT NEW REGIME YOU HAVE.

BACK INSIDE... WELL, MR. McSMITH, YOUR UNDERPANTS ARE TOO TIGHT, WHICH HAS LED TO MOISTURE LEVELS BEING UNACCEPTABLE, AND TO A MODERATELY HIGH CLEFT FLUFF READING.

OH DEAR.

DON'T WORRY SIR, OF COURSE THERE WILL BE NO PUNISHMENT. STEP TO THE REAR OF THE UNIT, YOU WILL FIND A RECEPTICLE FOR YOUR PANTS, THEN WE WILL CLEANSE YOUR BUTTOCKS WITH CHEMICALS TO HELP PREVENT ANY FURTHER PROBLEMS FOR YOU.

THANKYOU. THIS IS A PLEASANT SURPRISE.

IN ANOTHER BOOTH... DON'T BE AFRAID. WHEN HE'S FINISHED MR. BOTTOMY-WOTTOMY'S GOT A GOODY-FILLED FUN-PACK FOR YOU TO TAKE HOME!

WAAAH!

IT'S ALRIGHT LOVE. THIS WON'T TAKE TOO LONG.

I DON'T LIKE THIS HORRIBLE MAN! HE SAYS HE'S A CLOWN, BUT I THINK HE'S REALLY SCARY.

PRESENTLY...

PILE OINTMENT | SMEARED TOILET PAPER | EXCESS BUTTOCK HAIR | CLEFT FLUFF | SOILED UNDER...

NOW THEN... LET ME SEE...

HELLO LOVE. HOW WAS IT FOR YOU?

TOO TIGHT UNDERPAN...

THEY SAID MY BUTTOCKS WERE A LITTLE FLABBY AND MY KNICKERS WERE TOO OLD.

OOH. THAT DOESN'T SOUND TOO GOOD.

WELL, THAT'S WHAT I THOUGHT, I WAS EXPECTING TROUBLE, BUT THEY'VE GIVEN ME A DIET SHEET, AN EXCERCISE VIDEO AND SOME MARKS AND SPENCER VOUCHERS.

WHAT?... HELP, GIFTS AND NO TROUBLE?

THAT IS CORRECT. NOW I MUST PAINT YOUR BUTTOCKS WITH CHEMICALS.

? !

TEN MINUTES LATER...

GOOD DAY TO YOU.

WELL I SAY, THAT WAS A PAINLESS EXCERCISE.

THAT NIGHT... I MUST SAY IT WAS SPLENDID TO SEE THE BOTTOM INSPECTORS BEHAVE LIKE THAT. IT'S CERTAINLY GOOD TO KNOW THAT THERE IS STILL SOME GOOD TO BE FOUND IN THE WORLD, DARLING.

YES.

WE TOOK THE LIBERTY OF LETTING OURSELVES IN. I HOPE YOU DON'T MIND.

EEEEEEEEEEEEEEK!

LET ME EXPLAIN...YOU SEE OUR CARAVAN TODAY WAS WHAT YOU MIGHT CALL A LITTLE... DECEPTION.

YOU FIEND!

WELL, I LIKE TO THINK SO... BUT SAVE YOUR EMOTIONS...

...THE INSPECTIONS GAVE US VITAL INFORMATION ON SERIOUS BOTTOM CRIMINALS, YOURSELVES INCLUDED OF COURSE...

...THE CHEMICALS USED TO PAINT YOUR CHEEKS WERE IN FACT RADIOACTIVE TRACING AGENTS, WHICH WE USED TO FOLLOW YOU, AND EVERYONE ELSE STUPID ENOUGH TO HAVE COME TO US TODAY...

BUT WHY?

...YOU COULD HAVE ARRESTED US THERE AND THEN TODAY?!

THERE IS A LOGICAL EXPLANATION OF COURSE. WE WANTED TO COME TO YOUR HOMES SO WE COULD TAKE YOU AND YOUR FAMILIES, AND YOUR NEIGHBOURS, AND ANYONE ELSE WE DECIDE TO FOR THAT MATTER TO THE BOTTOM CORRECTION CENTRES!

BOTTOM ROUNDUP SQUAD OBI

BOTTOM ROUNDUP OBI

WHERE YOU WILL RECEIVE THE ULTIMATE PUNISHMENT AT THE HANDS OF THE BOTTOCUTIONER!!

103

A BIT ON THE OT

Doris Stoke-Manderville is a medium with a difference. For when spirits contact her from the other side, it's not to pass messages on to their loved ones. It's for sex!

And Doris boasts a host of ghost celebrities among her lovers from beyond the grave. Over a period of several years she claims that the late stars of showbusiness have, quite literally, been putting their willies up her. And now she exclusively reveals the sexy secrets of the celebrity spooks who regularly go hump in the night.

'Dead stars have been putting the willies up me for years', says Doris

❛My intimate sexual experiences all began quite by accident. I had been admitted to the chiropodists for a routine operation on my toe nail. The next thing I knew I was suddenly aware of being outside of my body, looking down on the chiropodist who was operating on my foot. There seemed to be some sort of panic, and the nurse was rushing around the room looking for some scissors.

BALD

I remember clearly looking down on the chiropodist, and noticing a small bald patch on the top of his head. Later he confirmed that he had a small bald patch, something which I could not possibly of known had I not been floating above him in that surgery as my life lay in the balance down below. I now realise that I underwent a near death experience on that day, and my memories of it are still vivid.

I was floating through a tunnel. Ahead of me I could see a light. I headed towards it and found myself emerging from beneath a quilt. I was in bed. And stranger still, there was a tall, dark man next to me who I immediately recognised as being Bernie Winters, the late TV comic.

Bernie's bed was the scene of a 'Heavenly' experience

I had always been a fan of Bernie's, and I offered no resistance as he took me in his arms and grinned. His big, goofy smile was unmistakable. I was in Heaven – quite literally – as we made love for what seemed an eternity.

Afterwards Bernie lit a cigarette and turned to me. "You have to go back", he said. "You still have a life to live". I knew that he was right. As I crawled back beneath the sheets I glanced back and saw Bernie grinning bravely. His eyebrows were raised in that silly smile, but he could not hide the tear which was running down his cheek.

LITTLE

Crawling back down the dark tunnel I suddenly found myself back in the chiropodist's surgery. The nurse was offering me a cup of tea. She explained that there had been complications, and that my toe may feel a bit sore for a few days. In a way I felt glad to be alive, but at the same time sad that I had to leave Bernie.

GOLDEN

The next time I had sex with a ghost was in my bedroom a few weeks later. I'd gone to bed early while my husband watched the football. Suddenly I heard the sound of chains dragging on the stairs. Then a dark figure appeared in the doorway. I nearly had a *Shear Heart Attack* when I saw who it was! Because there in my bedroom stood Freddie Mercury, dressed in full bondage gear, complete with leather cap, rubber pants, a dog collar and lots of chains.

GEORGE

I'd always fancied Freddie but didn't think his ghost would be interested in girls. I couldn't have been more wrong! He was all over me, kissing every inch of my naked body.

BILLY

Before things went too far I asked him if he'd mind wearing a Durex. I believe in safe sex, even with ghosts. He was the perfect gentleman, and got one out

MERCURY - used rubber

COOPER - 'Magic tricks'

of my husbands top draw. Being a ghost his cock was a bit see through, but between the two of us we just about managed to get it on.

FREDDIE

When it comes to sex Freddie *was the champions* alright. He was wonderful. Afterwards he took off the Durex, tied a knot in it and threw it on the floor. Then, after wiping his ghostly cock on the curtains he walked through the wall and was gone. Curiosity got the better of me and I picked up the rubber just to see what ghoulish gunk looked like. But to my amazement it was completely empty. In fact it was still in its packet in the draw where my husband had left it.

PROOF

Now you try explaining that to me! If that's not proof of ghosts shagging me then I don't know what is.

COOPER

They say that there are sixty-nine love making positions in the Karma Sutra. Well I discovered number seventy the night magician Tommy Cooper visited me in my bedroom! You see, ghosts can take their heads off if they want to. And magician ghosts can do practically anything they like with their bodies.

BREMNER

Well, me and Tommy had only been at it for a few moments when suddenly he popped his head off and tucked it under his arm. My hair turned white with shock. Minge hair that is! Anyway, Tommy was exactly that! (Magic that is.) He would be making love to me from behind while his hands fondled me passion-

ately. First one, then two, then three! Eventually there were half a dozen hands groping every inch of me at once.

CHARLTON

Occasionally he'd stop and produce a rabbit from his backside, or saw me in half. I had never enjoyed sex so much. Then, after what seemed like an eternity, we reached the most thrilling climax I have ever known. As Tommy made love to me my body shook with ecstacy, while in the mirror I could see his head on the dressing table, wanking furiously. That was a night I'll never forget in a hurry, I can tell you!

HUNTER

At first my husband used to object to me having sex with the dead stars, then he seemed to get quite turned on by the idea and suggested that the next time I did it he should come along and watch. So the following night I arranged to have a sexy threesome with Laurel and Hardy and my husband came along and brought a camera.

LORIMER

My husband snapped away like mad while Laurel and Hardy took turns fulfilling me. Afterwards the fat one looked at the sheets and said "That's another fine mess you've made on the bedclothes", while the thin one scratched his head and started crying.

CLARKE

The following day my husband got the film developed, but when he went back to collect it he thought for a minute he'd got the wrong pictures. All you could see was me on the bed, apparently having passionate sex with myself.

★★★★★★★★★★★★★★★★★★★★★★★★★★★★★★★★★★★★★★★

...HER SIDE

Hubby and I *liked* it hot with Monroe!

Stan and Ollie (above) joined Doris for a sexy threesome.

ALL THE FUN OF THE SCARE!

Sextet of ging gang gooly gooly gooly gooly gang bang ghouls tried to pull a ghost train up my tunnel of love!

Monroe – did 'lesbian'

from behind, and kissing every inch of my own naked body. The mystery was solved when we noticed an advice sticker on one picture, pointing out that ghosts don't show up in photographs.

JONES

After that my husband suggested we try a bit of girl on girl action with some lady ghosts, and asked me to put on a lesbian show with Marilyn Monroe. I summoned her to the bedroom using a glass and some playing cards. At first we were both nervous, and I admitted to her that I had never done lesbian. She said it was her first time too.

MADELEY

Anyway, we did a topless show for my husband, and I licked a sausage while Marilyn kissed my bottom. Suddenly a cold ghostly draught blew her skirt up, just like in that film. My husband got so excited he tried to join in. But he was forgetting that I have special powers to have sex with ghosts. If a mere mortal like him tries to touch a ghost, his hand just goes through them as if they aren't there.

GILES

So my poor husband ended up falling flat on his face and banging his head on the wardrobe! I couldn't stop laughing, and even Marilyn saw the funny side. Unfortunately however, that was not the only time when things got a little out of hand.

BATES

As a child I'd always been too scared to ride on a ghost train. But not nearly as scared as I was the night half a dozen ghosts decided to pull their very own ghost train – on me!

LECTER

Apparently several ghosts had been at a party in Heaven and had taken a lot of drink on board. You could say that they were in high spirits! In fact I've never seen six ghosts as pissed as they were. Anyway, they rolled up through my bedroom wall at two o'clock in the morning and I immediately knew what they were after.

KRUGER

Well I was having none of it. I'm as saucy as the next person, don't get me wrong. But I draw the line at having sex with six drunken ghosts all at once.

JASON

Luckily I had my wits about me and I told them I had the painters in. They took it in good spirits and I made them all a cup of coffee and we sat and watched TV until their ghost taxi arrived. It didn't honk the horn or ring the bell. It just drove in through the wall with a ghostly 'wooosh!' sound and hovered above the coffee table.

KYLIE

All six ghosts piled into the taxi, but the driver wasn't having it. He said he was only licensed to carry five ghosts, and someone had to get out. Luckily one of them – I think it was 'carry on' actor Sid James – said he needed some fresh air, and offered to walk back to Heaven. Eventually I got rid

of them, but only after lending them the taxi fare home!

CRAIG

Another scare I had was when I got pregnant by a ghost. It was Dirty Den who did it. He'd just been murdered in EastEnders, having got Michelle pregnant. Then he turned up in my bedroom while my husband was out and smooth talked his way into bed with me. I should have known better. Anyway, I found out I was expecting and told him so. But he didn't want anything to do with it.

Den – ghost baby father

In the end I decided to have an abortion. Ghost abortions are a bit like killing a Dracula. You can't get them on the National Health, that's for sure! My husband went down the butchers and got a steak and some garlic, and we used them to kill it during daylight hours.

Thinking about it now perhaps I should have had the ghost baby, because a friend of mine who is a nurse says that ghost babies simply walk through your tummy instead of coming out *down below,* so it doesn't actually hurt at all.

MRS MANGLE

Sometimes my husband and me lie awake at nights and cry thinking about my ghost baby that we killed with steak. But perhaps with all the murders and everything the world today would not have been a good place to bring up a ghost baby.

I guess that ghost baby is in Heaven now. Wherever it is I know it understands that what we did was for the best.

GHOSTBONKERS!

A great many people have claimed to have been the victims of sex attacks by ghosts. In fact, in certain parts of South America women are twice as likely to be raped by a ghost (or a space alien) than by an ordinary man. But ghost sex fiends look nothing like Frankenstien's monster, Dracula or any of the other fictional ghosts we see on the cinema screen.

SPECTRES

The scientific term for sexy spectres is an *incubus,* and one theory is that their 'bodies' or shapes are made up of a kind of chemical energy know as erectoplasm. Some of these ghosts take human form, others look like small green electric clouds that whizz about the place breaking things.

MARTENS

In the past the police have often been accused of scepticism and a lack of sympathy when dealing with cases of ghost rape, and there has never been a successful conviction of a dead rapist in British legal history. However a new postal helpline has recently been set up to provide help and support for

> By our SCARY GHOSTS CORRESPONDENT
> **BLAKEY**
> Off On The Buses

the victims of ghost sex. If you have been attacked by a ghost, write to the following address explaining in as much detail as possible exactly what happened. *Ghost Sex Helpline,* P.O. Box 1PT, Newcastle upon Tyne, NE99 1PT.

Due to the volume of mail received it may not be possible in all cases to send a reply. We reserve the right to publish (in edited, abridged, or in totally unrecognisable form) all submissions received.

TOP JOKE

I CAN'T EAT ANY MORE OF THIS DARLING.

YOUR EYES ARE BIGGER THAN YOUR BELLY.

Cliff's nuts set to blow

A peaceful Surrey town is today facing a jisolm cataclysm. For sex experts are warning that Weighbridge could soon be engulfed in Britain's first ever tidal gunk wave.

Scientists fear that the bollocks of one of the town's most celebrated residents – Cliff Richard – could explode if the popular singer does not have sex soon. And the resulting 'Pompeii' style disaster could reduce parts of Surrey to a spunky slurry.

BIOLOGY

Cliff, the seemingly ageless Peter Pan of Pop, claims to have been celibate for many years, and biology experts fear a potentially deadly build up of body fluids in his undercarriage could soon reach bursting point.

As nearby residents prepare to protect their homes against flood damage with sandbags and tons of tissue paper, the question on everyone's lips is 'Will Peter Pan's Plumbs go Pop?'

PHYSICS

Weighbridge council officials were last night setting up an emergency control centre, and the army are understood to be on full alert. Late last night an eerie silence hung over the town as anxious residents hoped and prayed that the singer would either get his leg over, or experience a nocturnal emission before it is too late.

By our Chief Knackers Correspondent
BUCK
off the High Chaparal

What makes a star's knackers blow up?

Exploding celebrity knackers is not a new phenomenon in Britain. As recently as 1989 fans of celibate comedian and author Stephen Fry were stunned when his left nut appeared to explode during a book signing session at a shop in Cambridge. No-one was hurt, although there was substantial damage to several books and a carpet.

CHEMISTRY

The medical profession has been aware of the condition, often referred to as Volatile Knackers, since before the turn of the century. But little contemporary research has been carried out in the field, and there is no course of treatment readily available to sufferers, other than having a wank.

FREE PERIOD

The problem arises when semen, which is constantly produced in the male adolescent body, is not ejaculated by the penis due to a lack of any sexual activity. Failure to 'chuck your muck' in this way can lead to the development of the early symptoms of the condition, including a 'stiffy', and 'nuts like two tins of Fussells milk'.

Bob names the day for charity spectacular

Stars whose surnames are types of weather are to be invited to turn out in a charity football match to pit their soccer talents against stars whose surnames are types of cars.

The Weather versus Car soccer star challenge was the brainwave of charity organiser Bob Johnson who hopes that the all star event will help raise millions of pounds for research into baldness.

GENERAL PUBLIC

"Stars as well as the general public are often struck down with this terrible hair losing condition, and it is therefore appropriate that big name stars like John Thaw, David Frost and Gareth Hale should take part in this spectacular fund raising event."

THE BEAT

Bob's brainwave to pit celebrity weather against car surnames on the football field came to him after he had seen an item on the TV news read by Jon Snow in which MP Austin Mitchell had been interviewed.

"Unfortunately Austin Mitchell's christian name is car, not his surname, so he doesn't qualify for the team, but I am hopeful that Harrison Ford will be playing, as well as Tommy Cooper".

SPECIALS AKA

Invitations have already been sent out to four celebrities in all whose surnames are also types of weather, and two whose surnames are a kind of car.

"It's early days yet, and whilst no-one has actually

Frost yesterday followed by Thaw early this morning.

accepted the invitation at this stage, I'm confident that we'll have a bumper turn out on the day, and a really exciting game", Bob told us.

SELECTOR

As well as the match, Bob will be selling balloons. The fun kicks off at 3pm on Saturday 26th June 1993 at Fulchester Recreation Ground. Bob says that any stars willing to take part, especially those whose surname is a type of car, should contact him at his work number which is Fulchester 577985, extension 427.

THE ADVENTURES OF **STAVROS** WITH T.V.'s FUNNYMAN Harry Enfield

HALLO MATEY PEEPS. I'M A MAKE A BLADDY KEBAB FOR HER INSIDA DE DOORS. AND ATTA DE WEEKEND, SHE SAY I CAN GO UPA DE ARSE...

COS THEY PLAY DE QUEENS' PARK RANGE!

(INNIT?!)

WELL, THAT'S IT FOR THIS WEEK, MATEY PEEPS! BYE

Copyright © Harry Enfield. Not to be used without permission

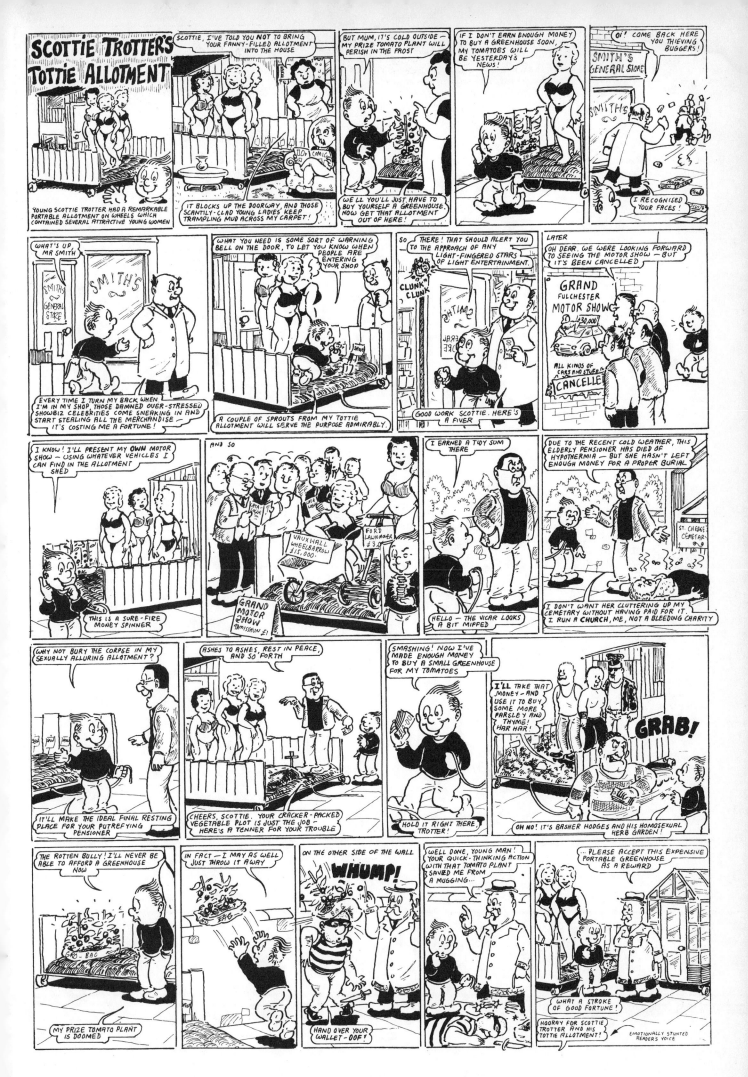

111

LetterBocks

Let's get back to Victorian values

This Government are all in favour of a return to Victorian values. Well if any cunt in the cabinet wants to sell me their house, I'll give them five hundred pounds ten shillings and sixpence for it.

W. I. Finial
Putney

Every time I open my wardrobe there seems to be more traffic cones in it than there was before. It would be different if men had periods, etc.

Ben Elton
Hampstead

No Winner situation

I was concerned to hear that film director Michael Winner must undergo heart surgery. What a great loss it would be to the British film industry if this overweight, pointy nosed, right wing, opinionated, sex maniac were to pop his clogs.

R. Valley
Cardiff

Why do people in Cilla Black's 'Surprise Surprise' programme always look surprised? You'd think that the title of the show would provide them with a couple of pretty strong hints as to what might happen.

Mrs P. Morley
Northwich

Using lead free petrol is hardly a great sacrifice to make in order to save the planet. Some of these so-called environmentalists should try using lead free pencils.

P. Northwich
Morley

Student debate

I read with interest Mr A. Pelling of Oxford's letter ('Top Tips', issue 62) in which he implies students are more intelligent than others among us who have not benefited from further education. However, I'd appreciate it if he, or any other student, could answer the following point. If you little cunts are so fucking bright, how come you can't read the 'Do Not Touch' signs in our hi-fi shop?

Nick & Ian
Cornwall

Apologies for interupting this adult humour letters page, but I was wondering whether any of your readers could help us. We are collecting B.P. 'Options', Esso 'Tiger' and Texaco 'Star' fuel tokens to raise money to buy a much needed estate car to help our children get out and about. If readers send us their surplus tokens we will use them to raise cash at future fund raising events.

Mrs May Henderson
East Park Home
Glasgow

Send your tokens, or donations, or estate cars, to East Park Home for Infirm Children, 1092 Maryhill Road, Glasgow, G20 9TD. (Registered charity no. CR18208).

I find motorway driving much more enjoyable now that I own an automatic car as I am now able to tap my left foot to the music on the radio without any interruptions. I also tilt my head from side to side in time with the music, pausing occasionally to check my mirrors.

R. Soning
London

As a disabled driver I am fed up with other motorists parking in our reserved spaces in supermarket car parks. Perhaps if the supermarkets would allocate us spaces in a far corner of the car park, well away from the supermarket entrance, able bodied people would not be tempted to park in them.

A. Smith
Putney

They're all a bunch of lesbians

I'm all in favour of the Government forcing absent fathers to pay ludicrous amounts towards the maintenance of their children. It will make them think twice in future before having sex with a lesbian, which I believe most of these single parent mothers are. The rest are, of course, prostitutes, and perhaps they should be taxed on the money which the fathers no doubt paid them in the first place for having sex.

C. Pot
Clapham

Shut up you old fuss pots

Don't listen to old folks complaining about VAT on their fuel bills. These people will always find something to complain about. If it wasn't their heating bills it would be something else, like the size and shape of decimal currency, or the frequency of bus services.

D. Pipe
Halifax

I agree with Mr Pipe's letter (issue 63). I am also in favour of taxing old people on their fuel bills. My wife and I call it the 'Mattress Tax', because we all know that pensioners have been hoarding cash in their mattresses for years. Well they'll not need it where they're going, will they? So stop moaning and cough up.

B. Chimney-Stack
Aldershot

Having to wear red paper poppies in our lapel for a week seems like an awful lot of bother to go to just to remind ourselves of Rememberance Sunday. Wouldn't it be a better idea for the newsreaders to remind us about Rememberance Sunday the day before, like they do when the clocks go back. Then all the money we spend on poppies could be saved and given to charity instead.

W. Slates
Rhyll

If a kitten's stomach is only the size of the tip of your thumb – as is claimed on the current 'Whiskas' TV advertisment, perhaps one of your readers could explain how they are able to manufacture turds somewhat larger than a man's fist.

G. Crocker
Fareham

They say you can't teach an old dog new tricks. Well my wife's 68, ugly as a boot, and yesterday I taught her how to set fire to her farts.

R. Tile
Battersea

Where are they now?

Tristram as TV viewers remember him, and (below) how he is today.

Whatever became of actor Nicholas Bond-Owen, better known as Tristram, the boy next door, in Thames TV's 'George & Mildred' series. So asked Ian Wheelclamp of Swindon.

Well Ian, Nicholas, who began playing Tristram at the age of seven, drifted out of the acting profession after 'George & Mildred'. A millionaire at the age of ten, he invested most of his earnings from the series in a goldfish farm in Oxfordshire which failed in 1979, leaving him penniless. Now 74, Nicholas owns a small printing business in his home town of Ashford, Middlesex, where he lives alone, but quite happily.

"I have no regrets. I enjoyed my time as Tristram. Those were wonderful days, and I have marvellous memories of them. But I'm just as happy now," he told us. But does he ever contemplate a return to acting? "I've had offers of pantomimes over the years, and a bit of TV, but I don't miss acting at all to be quite honest. I'm perfectly happy without it".

** If you'd like to know what happened to a star of the past, write to 'Where are they now' at our Letterbox address.*

Obscure Seventies Pop Group Baggage Stuck in Taxi Boot Joke No.42

WHEN THIS GETS OUT SPARKS ARE GONNA FLY.

AIRPORT

WANKING ON THE MOON!
Sting plans £100 billion space sexperiment

Sex crazy pop millionaire Sting is set to turn his back on the pop charts – and head instead for the moon!

For the love bonkers former Tyneside schoolteacher is planning a journey into space – in order to improve his sexual performances. And that, despite the fact that he is already better at having sex than anyone else in the world.

NUTTY

Screw nutty Sting, who has admitted he can 'do it' for anything up to five hours without going off, puts his amazing *sexcess* at knobbing down to yoga exercises which he and actress wife Trudy Styler do every day. But the 42 year old shag buff believes he can improve his love making technique by practising special *weightless sex* in space.

PICNIC

And so the hump loopy loveboat has commissioned a special rocket to be built which will take him, together with wife Trudy and a cargo of condoms, on a voyage of *sexploration* which could cost the poke potty popster anything up to £100 billion.

According to a showbiz insider, Sting hopes that in a weightless space environment, such as the moon, his bottom will be free to 'float', rather than go up and down and up and down, and consequently love making will be a longer, more gentle experience.

LION

Little research has been done into sex in space, although the first man on the moon, Neil Armstrong, was scheduled to have an experimental wank in 1969. However, he chickened out in the newsagents and bought a car magazine instead of a jazzmag, and returned to Earth not having experienced a weightless ham shank.

Pop star Sting could be disappointed with space sex, according to one leading space boffin. For rather than finding his bottom 'floating' in a weightless space environment, he may find it heavy, and difficult to lift.

IRON

For professor Wilfred Saltzeimer of Cambridge University's Department of Astrology has written several papers on the subject of sexual activity in space, and is the author to the book 'How Martians Have Sex'.

ZION

In his book Professor Saltzeimer compares the Martian penis to a bottle of tomato ketchup. "Martians are red, and so is their sperm. In fact, Martians' sperm looks just like tomato ketchup, and the male Martian reproductive organ is much the same shape as a ketchup bottle. In the same way that it is often necessary to bang the bottom of a ketchup bottle to make the ketchup come

A typical space scene on the moon yesterday.

out, so a Martian has to make sudden, jerky movements of his bottom in order to shake out the seminal fluids, or ketchup, which come out in a large, uncontrolled dollop".

"Whilst Sting's penis is very probably not ketchup bottle shaped, and neither he nor his wife are Martian, I believe that similar 'banging' movements may be necessary to achieve ejaculation if they were to have sex on the moon", said the Professor yesterday.

Hollywood star's death riddle

Confusion yesterday surrounded the condition of Hollywood actor Raymond Burr after he failed to show up for a charity movie premiere.

Despite his recent death Burr, who shot to fame in the sixties as wheelchair bound TV detective Robert Ironside, was expected to show up for the lavish star studded Beverly Hills bash to raise money for monkeys. But close friends of the actor were stunned by his non-arrival, and doctors at the Los Angeles hospital where he died admitted they had no idea of the star's whereabouts.

However, late last night the mystery was solved when a colleague of the grey haired former Perry Mason star and closet homosexual revealed that Burr had checked in to a £600 a night Los Angeles cemetary under a false name shortly after being released from hospital.

Burr – 'Dead'

A spokesman for Burr's undertakers yesterday issued a brief statement. "I can confirm that Mr Burr has been admitted to the cemetary and that his condition remains dead", he told reporters who had gathered at the gate.

114

Lucy Hattersley's Husband

OH CLIFF. AT LAST WE ARE TOGETHER

ERM... LUCY. COULD I ASK YOU A SMALL FAVOUR?

Young Lucy Sugden first had doubts about her marriage to Cliff Collins when, on their wedding night, he began showing an interest in unusual sexual fantasies

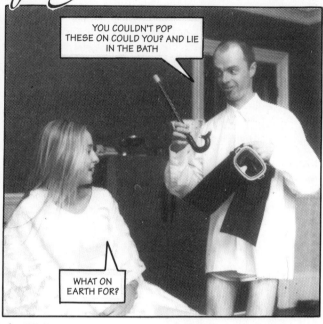

YOU COULDN'T POP THESE ON COULD YOU? AND LIE IN THE BATH

WHAT ON EARTH FOR?

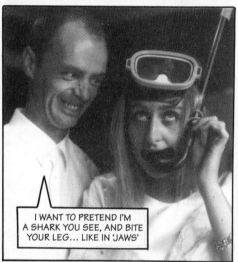

I WANT TO PRETEND I'M A SHARK YOU SEE, AND BITE YOUR LEG... LIKE IN 'JAWS'

The problem appeared to get worse...

CLIFF. WHY DO I HAVE TO DRESS UP AS A NUN EVERY TIME WE HAVE SEX

SHHH! THE NAZIES ARE COMING! WE MUST LEAD THE CHILDREN TO SAFETY, ACROSS THE ALPS

BUT WE DON'T HAVE ANY CHILDREN. AND WE WON'T GET ANY AT THIS RATE

DON'T BE SILLY. COME ON, LET'S GO AND SING A BIT IN THE GREENHOUSE

After a few weeks things appeared to be getting better, and as the couple settled into their new home Lucy became less concerned about her husband's behaviour.

ARE YOU ALRIGHT THERE MY LOVE?

YES DEAR. I'M JUST NAILING THIS PIPE

OUCH! MY THUMB

117

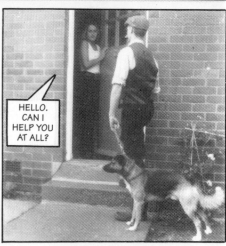

118

119

CD. ST. SD. SG. Photos by Colin D.

120

HER ROYAL RINGPIECE

Candid camera catches Queen

with her knickers down

Sneaky snapper Tom (left). The Queen is not amused.

A right Royal storm in a 'U' bend is brewing over lurid photographs taken from inside the Queen's lavatory.

For the sneaky snaps, snatched by a former Palace plumber, clearly show the Queen's arse perched proudly on the throne.

POSSESSION

The sensational pictures, which are now in our possession, are the work of plumber Tom Wilson, a former Palace employee whose job it was to look after the Queen's lavatories. The candid shots were taken using a secret camera hidden in the Queen's personal toilet, disguised as a number two.

SUPPLYING

Tom explained how his candid camera came about. "The Queen had asked me to mend her bog 'cos it hadn't been flushing properly. One particular dump had been reluctant to disappear, and kept bobbing about in the bowl. Anyway, as I looked at it, it occured to me that a camera hidden in the toilet would get a great view of the Queen's arse".

TRAFFICKING

Tom then set about the complex task of designing a camera that looked like a turd, and floated. "In the end I bought a top of the range £100 waterproof camera, tied a few corks to it, then disguised it by smearing a mixture of porridge and brown paint all over it. When I'd finished only the lens was visible, poking out the top".

MARMALADING

Tom tested the camera in his bath, making sure it floated, and that the lens would point up, directly at the Queen's bottom. "I rigged the shutter to open at the slightest trace of wind, so the gentlest of farts would set it off".

JAMMING

The next day Tom returned to the Queen's lavatory and dropped his secret floating camera down the pan. Then he waited. "I had never been as nervous in my life. I was convinced that the Queen would notice it and flush it away, or worse still fish it out for a closer look".

JAMMING

According to Tom's plan, once the camera had taken it's picture the Queen would then flush the lavatory. When she did he would pop down a nearby manhole to fish the camera out of the sewer. But after several hours standing knee deep in sewage beneath the Palace there was still no sign of a Royal flush.

JAMMING

"I later discovered that the Queen had used the toilet several times, but she hadn't flushed it once. Apparently Phillip encourages her to save water by only flushing it once every couple of days. So, after a particularly uncomfortable night I awoke at about 8.30 the following morning and heard a flush. Suddenly there was crap everywhere. I grabbed a couple of big logs, but they weren't the camera. Eventually I caught it, third time lucky."

JAMMING

Tom rushed to the local chemist to get his film developed straight away. But when he went back to collect the prints the following day, disaster struck. For there had been a mix-up, and his prints were handed to a police officer standing in the queue in front of him.

I WANNA

"He looked at the prints and immediately recognised the Queen's arse. Then he turned to me and asked if the photographs were mine. I thought I was done for. Then an idea sprang into my head. I said they were mine, but it was my *wife's* arse. I told him people were always mistaking my wife's arse for the Queen's."

JAM IT

"He seemed quite happy with this explanation and handed the prints over. By the time I got out of the shop I must have shit my pants about a dozen times, but it was worth it, I can tell you. On the bus home I just sat there looking at these lovely big pictures of the Queen's arse sitting on the bog. It was the most exciting moment of my life".

WITH YOU

We have obtained the pictures of the Queen's arse from Mr Wilson, *but we have no intention of publishing them*. Unlike certain other papers, we know where the line should be drawn between public interest and invasion of privacy. And the British public were quick to commend us on our brave stand.

"By refusing to print these pictures there is no doubt that the circulation of Viz will suffer. But I applaud this courageous moral stand", said one passer-by yesterday.

BIFFA BACON

CHRISTMAS EVE...

HOOW FATHA! AM WRITIN' ME CHRISMUSS LIST FOR SANTA...

TRAIN SET... FITBAAL BOOTS... TEN PUND HAMMA...

Y'CAN FORGET THAT SON

I'VE JUST FOOND THIS NURT WHAT'S FAALLEN DOON THE CHIMNEY. IT'S FOR YEE, AN' IT'S FROM SANTY CLAWS

EH?

IT SEZ "BIFFA IS NOT GERRIN' ANY PRESENTS THIS YEAR, COS E'S BIN A CUNT". SIGNED SANTA

EH? YA KIDDIN'!

NA. YA GETTIN' **FUCK ALL** OFF FATHA CHRISMUSS THIS YEAR UNLESS YORRA GOOD LAD.

AYE SON. YOU'LL HEFF T'START BEING **NICE** T'YA MUTHA AN' FATHA FROM NOO ON

SHORTLY...

FUCKIN' BRILLIANT! IT'S SNOWIN'

I FUCKIN' LOVE **SNUR**, ME

HEH HEH HEH! I'M GONNA BUILD ME A GEAT MASSIVE SNURMAN!

THERE NOO! PORFECT!!

HOY, BIFFA. WHAT Y'UP TO?

HOWAY FATHA, LEAVE ME SNURMAN ALAIRN Y'BASTAAD.

BUT BIFFA SON. THAT SNURMAN IS CALLIN' YEE A **PUFF**

EH?

WHO THE **FUCK** ARE **YOU** LOOKIN' AT?

GAN ON BIFFA. HE'S ASKIN' FORRIT!

GOT SOME SORT OF PROBLEM HAVE YA?

BOOF!

REET! THAT'S IT. YA **DEFINITELY** GERRIN' NEY PRESENTS OFF SANTA THIS YEAR FOR CLOBBERIN' YA MUTHA

BUT... BUT...

BUT I DIDN'T MEAN IT

I'LL TELL Y'WHAT THEN, SON. KISS ME BOOTS AN' I WIVN'T TELL SANTA!

HEH HEH HEH!

SLURP!

HOOF!

FARMER PALMER

YURR -JAAATHROW. THROW ZUMM MORE FIFTIES ON THE FOYRE.

WE BAIN' GOT NUN LEFT. 'ER'S ONLY TWENDIES -UN THEY'Z DON' BURRN ZO NOYCE LOIKE.

'EE REALOYZE WHAT THIS MEANS ZUNN? 'ER'S TOYME TO OPEN THEY FAAAAARM SHOP FER GRISMUZZ.

SHORTLY...

CONDEMNED FARM BUILDINGS PRIVATE! TRESPASSERS DOG'S WILL BE SHOT. NO TURNING FUCK OFF
GET OFF MY LAND

Palmer's FARM SHOP NOW OPEN FOR CHRISTMAS ~TREES ~ ORGANIC · PRODUCE · FREE-RANGE · TURKEYS · CHILDREN'S PLAY AREA · FREE PARKING etc.
everyone welcome

OOH LOOKGILES! A FARM SHOP! LET'S STOP AND GET ALL OUR CHRISTMAS PROVISIONS. THIS IS WHERE PEOPLE WHO LIVE IN THE COUNTRYSIDE BUY ALL THEIR PROPER HEALTHY FOOD!

UZISUZI TRUMPER

SIMULTANEOUSLY...

WOULD YOU LIKE MORE SUPERNOODLES WITH YOUR MINI-KIEVS DEAR?

THE COUNTRYSIDE

NO TA. I MUST LEAVE SOME SPACE FOR MY ANGEL DELIGHT...

ANYWAY...

NOICE MOWDER.

UZISUZI TRUMPER

YES. WE WENT FOR THE UZISUZI TRUMPER IN THE END BECAUSE THEY OFFERED THE OPTIONAL GOLDEN RETRIEVERS ON THE TURBO-DIESEL. OF COURSE, SERVICING'S A BIT STEEP NOW THAT THEY NEED A NEW OIL FILTER EVERY SIX MILES - THAT'S BECAUSE THEY'RE SO RELIABLE APPARENTLY - BUT THE FOUR WHEEL DRIVE IS USEFUL IF ANNABEL GETS STUCK ON THE VERGE DOING THE SCHOOL RUN.

WELL WORTH THE BEST PART OF 25 GRAND I MUST SAY.

HEH-HEH: MOIND EE, YOU'M WOULDN'D CAAATCH REAL CUNNDRY PEEBLE DROYIN' ONE O' THEEZ YURR BUGGERRZ.

REALLY?

AYE. UZZ PROBBER CUNNDAY FOLK CAAAN'D AFFORD SUCH FAAAANCY MODER GAAAARZ.

UZISUZI TRUMPER

'EE CAAN PAAAARK 'ER OVER THERE NEX' TER MOY ROLLERRRZ.

DADDY. CAN I GO AND SEE PETS' CORNER?

OF COURSE YOU CAN TOBY.

'ERZ FOIVE POUND.

JAAATHROW - TOYKE THIS YURR YUNG'UN TER ZEE PETS' COOOOORNERRRR.

OOH AAAR.

CAN I STROKE HIM PLEASE?

AYE. UNCLE SILAGE TOOK MOSD UV 'ER TEETH OOOUT WITH PLOYERZ TER GIVE THEY BAAADGERRRZ A CHAANCE.

DON' EE MOYND OL' BAAAARNEY. 'ER DON' SEE NOBODDY AAALL YURR. WE KEEPS 'ER CHAINED IN THEY STREAM UP BOY TOPPP FIELD TER STOPP THEY SHEEP ERZCAPIN'.

SNAP! SNARL!

'ER'Z CHEAPER 'UN BAAAR BED WOYRE, SEE?

BAAAD DOG BAAAD DOG

WHAM!
WHAM!

GO AWN. 'EE CAAAN STROKES 'ER NOOOW.

WHIMPER

124

125

FELIX AND HIS AMAZING UNDERPANTOMIME

THE VICAR IS ORGANISING A PANTOMIME TO RAISE FUNDS FOR A NEW CHURCH ROOF, SO I'M HELPING OUT BY TYPING THE SCRIPT... ON MY UNDERPANTS!

TAP-TAP-TAP etc.

DEC. '93

BAH! THE TYPEWRITER RIBBON HAS SNAPPED!

SNAP!

NOT TO WORRY. THESE SHREDDIES WHICH I SHITTED YESTERDAY DURING A HORROR FILM WILL MAKE AN IDEAL REPLACEMENT RIBBON!

THERE WE ARE! THE DARK, GRIMEY SKID MARKS LEAVE A CLEARLY LEGIBLE, IF NOT SLIGHTLY WHIFFY, BROWN IMPRESSION ON MY UNDERPANT PAPER!

TAP-TAP-SQUELCH etc.

LATER, AT THE CHURCH HALL...

THIS SCRIPT STINKS!

I THOUGHT IT WAS RATHER GOOD, ACTUALLY.

NO, IT LITERALLY STINKS! OF PISS AND EXCREMENT. WE CAN'T POSSIBLY USE IT. TAKE IT AWAY!

WE'RE PERFORMING PUSS IN BOOTS, SO I'VE VOLUNTEERED TO HELP WITH THE COSTUMES.

ONLY TROUBLE IS, WE DON'T HAVE ANY BOOTS FOR THE CAT... BUT I THINK I'VE GOT AN IDEA.

THERE NOW. A QUICK SCRIPT CHANGE TO 'PUSS IN PANTS', AND THE PROBLEM IS SOLVED!

AH, VICAR, I'VE BROUGHT MY CAT ALONG TO APPEAR IN THE PANTOMIME.

AH SPLENDID, MRS SLOCOMBE. FELIX WILL HELP YOU PUT ITS BOOTS ON.

BUT, SHORTLY...

CRUMBS. YOUR NICE FURRY PUSSY SMELLS OF FISH MRS SLOCOMBE.

HERE. IT WILL BE NICE AND WARM IN MY PANTS.

I DON'T KNOW WHAT YOU'RE UP TO IN HERE AND I DON'T WANT TO!

GO AND HELP THE VERGER WITH THE LIGHTING, FELIX. 'PUSS IN PANTS' INDEED!

ALL YOU DO IS MOVE THE LIGHT TO FOLLOW THE ACTORS AROUND THE STAGE. OKAY, FELIX?

OKAY. SEEMS SIMPLE ENOUGH.

HMMM. PERHAPS I COULD BRIGHTEN THE SHOW UP A BIT BY USING MY BRIGHT RED UNDERPANTS AS A LIGHT FILTER.

THERE WE ARE! THE VICAR WILL BE IMPRESSED!

MEANWHILE, ON STAGE...

ONLY 50 MILES TO LONDON AND STILL NO SIGN OF DICK...

GOODNESS GRACIOUS!

GASP!

?

FELIX! GET YOUR GENITALIA OUT OF THAT BEAM AT ONCE!

BOOM!

VIZ 63 CD/ST + GPD/SD / LEW STRINGER.

SORRY VICAR. THE HEAT FROM THE LIGHT IGNITED A POCKET OF FART WHICH HAD BECOME TRAPPED IN THE 'Y' SHAPED PISS HATCH IN MY TROLLEYS.

YOU BUFFOON. NOT ONLY HAVE YOU WRECKED THE PANTO, YOU'VE ALSO RUINED WHAT WAS LEFT OF THE CHURCH ROOF!

BAH! NOW IT'S SNOWING. AND THANKS TO YOUR UNDERP-ANTICS WE HAVEN'T RISEN FUCK ALL TOWARDS THE ROOF REPAIR FUND. I HAVE NO OPTION BUT TO CANCEL CHRISTMAS.

UNLESS YOU HAVE ANY BRIGHT IDEAS...

GUESS W-W-W-WHAT READERS. MY UNDIES MAKE A P-P-P-PERFECT REPLACEMENT R-R-R-ROOF!

HEY, LOOK UP THERE. YOU CAN SEE HIS COCK.

AND HIS ARSE.

126